You are

Cherishable!

Cherishable

**An Illuminating
Guide for Caregivers
and Patients**

Julie J. Wylie

POND READS • SAINT PAUL, MINNESOTA

Edited by Angela Wiechmann
Proofread by Ruthie Nelson
Critical Read by Betsy Barthelemy
Production Editor: Hanna Kjeldbjerg
Author Photo by Chelsea Madsen

ISBN: 978-1-64343-972-3
Library of Congress Catalog Number: 2021907818
Printed in the United States of America
First Printing: 2021
25 24 23 22 21   5 4 3 2 1

Pond Reads Press
939 Seventh Street West
Saint Paul, MN 55102
(952) 829-8818
www.BeaversPondPress.com

To order, visit www.JulieJWylie.com.
Reseller discounts available.

Contact the author at www.JulieJWylie.com to share your story and for more information about speaking engagements, book club discussions, freelance writing projects, and interviews.

I dedicate this book in loving memory to my mother, Patricia Anne Keenan Johnson.

Mom, I remember when the idea of a book occurred to both of us over the phone in 2008. I was driving to work, and you were at home in Mankato, living with cancer. The idea of a book felt larger than us then, and it still does now. I know that whether you are physically here or not, you are aware of this book. You will guide hearts to be touched and inspired by it, just as you guide my heart daily.

God is like electricity. A house can be wired for it, but if there aren't any light fixtures, what good does that do? If God is seen as electricity, then we are His lamps. It doesn't matter the size of the lamp, or its shape, or design. All that matters is that it gets plugged in. It doesn't matter who we are, or what our gifts are. All that matters is that we are willing to be used in His service. Our willingness, our conviction, give us miraculous power. The servants of God bear the imprint of their Master.

Lamps without electricity cast no light, and electricity without lamps casts no light either. Together, however, they cast out all darkness.

—MARIANNE WILLIAMSON

Contents

Foreword

The phone call came. "Janae, I'm in the ambulance, and we're on the way to the hospital. We found out Mom has stage IV lung cancer." My heart dropped and tears welled in my eyes as my soul sister Julie shared this shocking news.

This phone call began the three-year journey I experienced with Julie. On this journey, Julie spent a tremendous amount of time caring for her beloved mom, Patty Johnson. But the journey was about more than basic caregiving. It was about Julie taking intentional steps to honor her mother before, during, and after her death. As you read Julie's story, you'll discover how this was the most heart-wrenching but also the most spiritually enlightening experience for her.

It was an incredible spiritual experience for both of us, actually. It exemplifies one of the reasons why we consider each other soul sisters. We were drawn together because of our faith, and it's our faith that continues to bind us together today.

It was an honor that God used me to help Julie during her journey. There were many "Godcidences" that gave us chills and let us know we were being led by divine guidance.

For example, I met Julie for a walk one day, and I happened to bring a book about how to write your legacy. Somehow, I knew she needed it. Little did I realize that Julie had heard a whisper the night before that she was to write her mother's eulogy.

Then there was the time I was at lunch with a friend and happened to see Julie walking by outside the window. I hadn't realized her office was right by that restaurant.

I ran outside to say hello—only to realize I had been guided by the angels to be at that exact restaurant at that exact time so I could comfort Julie. It was the day she found out her mother would need to transition into hospice.

While hugging Julie out there on the sidewalk, I asked God what more I could do for her. Instantly, I was inspired to contact her other close friends, Nancy Gnos and Holly Locher, to start an "angel network." Our mission was to support Julie during the last stages before her mother's passing.

As Anaïs Nin explained, "Life shrinks or expands in proportion to one's courage." The word *courage* comes from the Latin word for "heart." And courage is exactly what I saw grow in Julie. The strength she showed when facing one of the hardest experiences a person goes through—the death of a parent—was indeed courageous.

I'm blessed in that my parents are still living. I know I'll face their deaths someday, and I pray I'll do it with as much heart, love, and grace as Julie did. But before that time arrives, I want to be proactive so I can capture my parents' legacy and be prepared for the journey of their passing. Julie has inspired me to cherish this time and use it wisely.

It's an honor to help Julie share her story with the world. This book is a must-read for all adult children and their parents. So many of us don't know what to do when a loved one dies or faces a terminal illness. *Cherishable* encourages families to have much-needed and heartfelt conversations about preserving one's legacy before it's too late.

Julie understands that the greater the relationship, the greater the need to commemorate it. Everything she did to commemorate her mother, as you'll read in this book, demonstrates her unfailing love for her. Our hope is that through Julie's examples, you'll be inspired to discover how you want to commemorate and cherish your loved ones as well.

—JANAE BOWER

A Note to My Family

How we leave others depends largely on how we prepare ourselves for death. When we can die with grateful hearts, grateful to God and our families and friends, our deaths can become sources of life for others.

—HENRI J.M. NOUWEN

Two months before Mom died, she and I were talking on the phone as I drove to work. We realized how many wonderful and inspired connections were happening even as we faced the decision for her to begin hospice. There was a feeling of disbelief and wonder at the synchronicities and the goodness coming our way during that uncharted time. The sentiment we both shared in that conversation was, "Wow, this could be a book."

And I might have said, "Maybe that's what I'll do after you die."

While this book is focused on Mom, I wish to salute both her and Grandma Keenan in this special note to you, my family. As I reflected on Mom's journey during the creative process for this book, I considered how her mother's choices during her own cancer journey paved the way and set an example of a beautiful death.

Teachers to the end, Mom and Grandma Keenan approached their deaths as their final teaching lessons on earth. Through their respective cancer journeys and deaths, they taught our family about the final stage of human life. They taught us how to cope, create, cry, laugh, react, plan, believe, honor, function, mourn, celebrate, cherish, and love.

While living, they had the foresight to chart out certain desires, so life would go as smoothly as possible as we navigated without them. They were decisive as they communicated what mattered to them.

They also had the hope and desire to live even in the face of dark diagnoses. They had created lives they wanted to see play out longer, yet they accepted their lot in life and made the best of it. They upheld the belief that finding joyfulness amid dying can create abundance and grace as well as lessen pain.

We can learn from their stories. They were great proof that how we spend our time during a terminal illness impacts the grief journey in many ways for the survivors. Well beyond their earthly lifetimes, Mom and Grandma Keenan continue to have positive impacts on family, friends, and future generations.

My hope is that by sharing our family's stories in this book, we may inspire others. Through these stories, I hope we can provide creative and meaningful legacy ideas so other families may cherish their loved one's character and all they continue to offer to the world long after their death. Perhaps other families will discover how to more intentionally use their time, resources, circumstances, and desires during a loved one's journey. I hope we can provide a light that illuminates a trying and uncharted path.

I believe God has called me to write this book to be a light guiding the way for others. It is an honor to share ideas that proved to be meaningful and effective for our family and friends.

The actions we took may perhaps ease suffering and inspire others to take actions applicable to their life and desires.

Let's use our time wisely and live without regrets.

Thank you for giving me the blessing to bring this book into the world so we may share this journey with others and help light their way.

I met Lynda Fishman, author of *Repairing Rainbows*, on a vacation cruise. I appreciate how she worded her approach to her book, and I share the same approach:

I have been faithful to what I remember and have recounted everything as honestly as possible. All incidents are described to the best of my recollection. None of the names have been changed.

—LYNDA FISHMAN

Introduction

There is not a right or wrong way to handle this end-of-life journey. There's no perfect book or thing to say. Every family is unique.

—FATHER JIM CASSIDY

"I am waiting to die."

I heard these words at a women's retreat at my church when the facilitator, Jane Leyden Cavanaugh, asked the group if anyone wanted to share details about their current phase in life. One of the retreat participants told us that her doctors had exhausted her cancer treatment options; now she was "waiting to die."

The news of this woman's diagnosis was unsettling enough in itself. From across the room, she didn't look any closer to death than the rest of us.

But what stuck with me was the word *waiting*.

As I sat there, I thought back to my experiences with three close family members on their hospice journeys. "I am waiting to die" was something they never once said. Not even when there were only a handful of days, hours, or minutes until death.

In those final moments, my loved ones said such things as "I need to rest" or "Let's have some quiet time" or "I'm going to close my eyes while you talk." Many times, they didn't say anything at all. They knew their time was limited, but they never referred to it as *waiting*.

Something inside me wanted to spring forth and ask this woman at the retreat how she was spending her time—her precious final time. Were there any conversations she yearned to have? Were her final wishes crystal clear? Was she taking steps to make life easier on her friends and family after she passed? Was she using her foresight to help make her loved ones' grief journey rich and loving, rather than unorganized and chaotic? Was she cherishing herself and honoring her own journey? Did she have a light guiding her way?

Maybe she was. But it made me wonder.

The experience with that woman was one of the elements propelling me to write this book. It stirred in me the question, *If you were terminally ill, would you see it as nothing more than "waiting to die"? Or would you want to use your time to benefit your legacy and the grief journeys of those you love?* As I contemplated those questions, I immediately thought of my mom.

My mother—Patricia Johnson, or Patty to many—had been the picture of health. She fixed us carob cookies in the 1970s, ate fruit and carrot sticks every day, never smoked, hardly drank alcohol, and was tall, active, and thin. I anticipated she would outlive many people in our lives. But then on Halloween 2005, doctors discovered she had advanced stages of lung cancer. Talk about a shocking and scary Halloween!

Right away, people said, "Miracles happen. Maybe a miracle will happen here." In their eyes, a miracle meant a cure.

But Mom was not cured. During her cancer journey, she went through multiple chemotherapy treatments, received radiation when it spread to her brain, lost her hair three times, eventually entered hospice, and ultimately died at home on September 17, 2008, at age sixty-five.

Through it all, I came to redefine miracles. She accepted life on life's terms, with open-mindedness, grace, hope, and faith. And we had the chance to cherish her life in the time she did have left.

That was the miracle.

In this book, I share Mom's story. It's not a play-by-play of her cancer treatments. It's a testament to how she chose to spend her time. How she strengthened her legacy. How she enriched all our lives during her final days—and beyond. She was such a great example of how we can use that "waiting" time productively for ourselves and others. She was a light illuminating a difficult path.

This book is a collection of vignettes—brief glimpses, moments, and memories—spanning from her diagnosis to the years after her passing. Pieced together, these vignettes share the story of how we all cherished Mom's journey and prepared for our own.

We had about three years with Mom between her diagnosis and her death. That foresight allowed us to begin with the end in mind. In fact, this is a concept featured in Stephen Covey's *The 7 Habits of Highly Effective People*. In his "Begin with the End in Mind" habit, he encourages us to begin any endeavor with a mission, a vision, and a values statement.

We can apply this idea to the end-of-life journey as well. My hope is that this book will be a light that helps others and their families envision the end *before* they actually come to it. That way, they can choose to cherish their time and enrich their legacies.

I fully understand that how Mom and our family chose to cherish this time might not be the same as how you choose to cherish yours. Every family has unique values, circumstances, and preferences. I don't expect you to follow our ideas to the letter; rather, I hope you will use them as springboards for your own.

If you too want to cherish this time with a loved one embarking on this journey, ask yourself, *How do I want to remember this time?* Because of the intentional choices I made during Mom's time, I now have loving, uplifting memories coupled with the pain of the loss. What I did and what she did while she was alive helped give me strength after she died.

Also ask yourself, *How can I be a gift, a light, to my loved one throughout this time?* I am confident we gave Mom a peaceful departure from this world, thanks to the faith, love, teamwork, and commitment of all involved. Remember your unique talents, and play to your strengths while you are considering how to be a gift. Each person can add to the journey in countless ways. There is no one "right" way. Focus on increasing confidence in yourself and others—even while allowing yourself to feel vulnerable during this difficult time.

When we get down to it, we are all "waiting to die." Some of us just happen to know the end is coming soon, that the wait won't be long. For those people and their loved ones, the wait is especially precious. I hope this book helps you make it count.

By daring to live while waiting to die, by being a light in the darkness, you will be able to cherish your time, yourself, and your loved ones.

Cherishable.

Part 1

*the shocking
diagnosis and
first decisions*

The supreme happiness of life is the conviction that we are loved; loved for ourselves—say rather, loved in spite of ourselves.

—VICTOR HUGO

Halloween

The Phone Call

The phone rang. It was the evening of Halloween, October 31, 2005. Mom's name came up on my cell. I had been expecting her call. She was at the hospital.

My brother, Michael, had married Julia that September. Shortly after the wedding, Mom didn't feel well. She had decreased energy. And she didn't get better, like she usually did after an illness.

A few days before Halloween, Mom was hospitalized due to breathlessness and a chronic cough. They were running tests to rule out everything from pneumonia, to a peanut caught in some pipe, to a range of other things. Lung cancer was not something we feared, though. At sixty-two years old, she was healthy, fit, and strong. She was a lifelong nonsmoker.

"Hi, Mom," I said, answering in our kitchen.

"I have some news to share with you. The tests revealed I have lung cancer." She minced no words.

I paused for only a second. "Well, Tom Rowland had lung cancer," I reasoned. "He had surgery, and now he's cancer-free. You can get over lung cancer."

"No, Julie," she responded. Her voice was definitive. "Not in my case. There is no operation that can cure me. They tell me it's terminal."

I sat down on the steps to our basement. My cries were soul wrenching, from deep within.

Before the phone rang, my husband, Justin, and I had been handing out candy to trick-or-treaters and chatting with our neighbors. Justin had decked out our yard with lots of Halloween décor.

After the call, we turned off all the lights, and Justin drove us eighty miles to the hospital in my beloved hometown of Mankato, Minnesota. I felt out of my mind. How could this be real?

I called my boss during the drive and let him know the diagnosis. I remember him assuring me, "Do what you need to do. We'll figure things out at work as needed."

Arriving at the hospital, we went right to Mom's room. I looked in and saw her sitting in a chair. Two of her closest friends, Suzann Voss and Pat Matejcek, were near her.

I rushed to her chair and sat at her feet, bawling with my head in her lap. She laid her hands on my back. Tender moments between mother and daughter.

"Oh, Mom."

"I know."

Dad and Justin stood by. We were together.

That was day one of the cancer journey, a very scary Halloween 2005.

When we have the courage to walk into our
story and own it, we get to write the ending.
And when we don't own our stories of failure,
setbacks, and hurt—they own us.

—BRENÉ BROWN

The Beginning of the Journey

The Initial Diagnoses

Mom's diagnosis on Halloween was stage IV lung cancer. The CAT scan showed fluid in the lungs, which turned out to be malignant.

The next day, a decision was made to transfer her via ambulance from Mankato to Rochester, Minnesota, for further evaluation. Rochester is the home of the Mayo Clinic. At the Rochester hospital, she would be in the Mayo system.

For the hour-and-a-half ride, I rode in the ambulance passenger seat while Mom rested in the stretcher in the back and was medically monitored. Other family members followed in their cars. During the ride, I talked on the phone with my soul sister Janae and cried.

After more testing in Rochester, the diagnosis was revised to stage IIIB lung cancer. The medical summary of diagnoses included adenocarcinoma of lung stage IIIB, pleural effusion, status post pleurodesis.

Doctors told us this was not a black-and-white situation. We were working within shades of gray. Mom was only sixty-two years old and the picture of health. It was such a brain twister that she could have cancer.

We asked about radon as a potential cause. The doctors explained that it's hard to quantitate the effects of radon. Sometimes only one person living in a house is affected.

Later, Dad would have the house tested for radon, and the results would reveal that levels were high enough to require a radon mitigation system. It made us suspect that radon played some part in Mom's cancer.

But as the doctors explained to us that day at Mayo, sometimes there is no obvious reason someone gets cancer. Getting caught up in the why would not change the diagnosis.

When I asked a doctor to help me understand what kind of timeline Mom had for life, he at first said it was difficult to define. I pressed him, though, admitting that I didn't know how to react to all this and wasn't sure what to do. That's when he divulged an estimate of six to twelve months as a typical range.

That was helpful. I knew I wouldn't need to take an immediate leave from work. I had time to make plans as to how to handle the coming days, weeks, and hopefully months.

Because she was healthy in many ways, Mom had treatment options. To extend her life, she made plans to start chemotherapy on November 30. She had a beautiful life, and she wanted to continue living. She wasn't eager to die.

She knew this was a chance to cherish her journey and prepare for what would follow for us all.

The earlier the information is communicated, with as much detail as possible, the better the change will be accommodated by those affected.

—PHIL GELDART

CaringBridge

The Touchstone and Cornerstone for Communicating

Once Mom was diagnosed with lung cancer, the news spread quickly within our family, friends, and community. The flowers, calls, cards, and prayers were helpful and encouraging yet overwhelming at the same time.

I was at my parents' home, watching television after a day at the hospital, when a good friend of the family called to see how Mom was doing. I didn't know where to start.

"What do you know so far?" I asked her.

She didn't know much, so I tried to summarize the current situation as best as possible. But I was already exhausted. I really didn't want to be on the phone.

This continued with more calls from more people. It was hard to gauge what any one person knew, so I found myself repeating the entire story every time.

My uncle, Kevin Keenan, called me one day. He acknowledged how much I was already doing to help Mom. He then suggested I take things a step further and start a CaringBridge website at www.caringbridge.org.

Kevin shared that a man at his golf club was ill, and the family had a CaringBridge site where people could read updates on how he was doing. Kevin said it a great way to spread the word without having to retell the story again and again.

Initially, I felt perturbed. Didn't he just say I was already doing so much? Why would he ask me to do *more?* If we did want a CaringBridge site for Mom, I thought maybe that should be someone else's job. I sat with that feeling a few days.

I did some research, though, to learn more about Caring-Bridge. It's a free nonprofit service, and they are focused on amplifying the love, hope, and compassion in the world by making each health journey easier.

When we were at the Mayo Clinic later that month, I noticed they had computers with internet access in the waiting room. We had a long wait for the next appointment, so I said to Mom, "You want one of those websites like Kevin mentioned?"

"*Ohhhhh*, yes!" she said in an expressive, enthusiastic tone. "Then people can learn from my story. I don't want others to go through what I'm going through with lung cancer."

Thus, we started the website that day.

Instead of seeing death as another significant part of our journey we usually deny death or try to avoid it. Most of us have little preparation for it so when we are facing death, our own or someone else's, we are overwhelmed.

—JANET O. HAGBERG

Planning the Funeral

In Case We Ever Need It

From the start, the doctors kept suggesting that Mom should "put her house in order." So, only a couple of days after her diagnosis, while still in the hospital, Mom started planning her own funeral.

She told us that after her funeral service, she wanted an open-invitation luncheon at the church hall followed by a family-only dinner at the Mankato Golf Club that evening. Between the luncheon and dinner, she wanted our family to have time to relax—nap, decompress, change into more casual clothes, and so on.

She envisioned the family dinner as a joyful, fun celebration for visiting. She did not want photographs of her on display or it to feel like a wake. She requested we have happy-hour food and beverages followed by a full dinner. In particular, she wanted it to be a different menu than at the luncheon. Rather than ask each family to pay individually, Mom stated that the dinner would be added to the general funeral expenses.

The golf club was a logical choice. It was a great local venue for private dinners. Our family has good memories of many birthdays, weddings, and anniversary celebrations there. Mom also mentioned having the dinner in a private hotel ballroom as a backup possibility. One way or another, she wanted the dinner at a venue where no one in the family had to prepare food or clean up. She knew we would be exhausted.

This is similar to what her family did after their mother's funeral. Mom knew that at the end of the funeral day, it was important for us to regroup as a family to tell stories, console one another, laugh, and relax.

While our family planned to hold this event at a golf club, another family might choose a wonderful restaurant, a park, or someone's garage. The point is to bring the family together in a special place so healing can continue within a smaller-group setting.

That was only the beginning of Mom's funeral planning. She officially started a funeral file folder just twelve days after her diagnosis. In the folder, she gathered her mother's funeral program and obituary, some well-written obituaries clipped from the newspaper, the mortuary price list, notes for her own obituary, notes for her Mass of Resurrection, and more. Using a file folder allowed her to collect and store these items in an organized way.

It also allowed her to treat funeral planning like a project. She could envision what she wanted at her funeral and spearhead what needed to be done to make it happen. She was businesslike and matter of fact. She had our family meet with representatives from the mortuary and the church, which was helpful.

As for me, I of course wanted Mom's funeral to be done according to her wishes. And I knew how important it was to make these plans while she had energy and focus.

Still, I struggled.

I didn't want to talk about her funeral—about her dying. I often found it disturbing and overwhelming. Some conversations—her chosen church and cemetery—were not difficult. But I didn't want to visualize her casket or imagine how it would feel to hear a certain song.

Sometimes I'd cry. Mom would be comforting, yet she'd also keep nudging to make progress on plans.

I found I could cope better if I simply went into "recording mode." In an almost mechanical, detached way, I would take notes about her ideas and directions. Sometimes, though, I needed to soften the language. I titled one document "Funeral Plans . . . In Case We Ever Need Them."

As difficult as the process was, there were some enlightening, collaborative moments. It was interesting to understand Mom's thought process about casket bearers or Communion ministers, for instance. Through these open conversations, I also learned where her preferences lay. For example, she was firm about the details of the golf club dinner, yet other details, such as the closing song at Mass, she never decided.

Consider it an honor if your loved one chooses to discuss funeral plans and last wishes with you. Your loved one needs someone to listen and record their desires. As hard as it can be, it is often an important part of mentally processing the final stage of life—for you and for your loved one.

If you agree to be the main recorder of these wishes, try to accept that other family members may not choose to take part in these difficult conversations—but that does *not* mean there's a lack of love. In fact, if your loved one asks for your help but you decide you're not the right person, consider recommending another person.

Some people want to make funeral plans in their last days; others want to make them immediately after their diagnosis. My mom lived almost three years after she made her funeral plans. She needed to talk about her last wishes immediately; only then could she focus on having hope and enjoying life.

In contrast, my grandpa Jerry Keenan communicated his wishes and delegated tasks during what ended up being the final days of his journey with lung cancer. Looking back, we now realize he maintained energy until he knew his plans were in good hands. Only then did he rest and relax. "I don't think people around here know how sick I am," he said toward the end. He died days later.

So, whenever your loved one wants to talk about plans, capture them. Even if you feel talking about funeral plans seems premature, rise to the occasion. Don't put it off. Your loved one often knows the timing better than anyone else.

On the other hand, if you're ready to discuss funeral plans but your loved one is not, trust that both desires have meaning. Rather than pressure your loved one into making plans, do some research and gather information on your own. Perhaps start your own funeral folder, which will likely become useful at the right time.

If you haven't made your bed, throw it away!
It's too late to make it now!

—CHRIS FLEMING

Vacuums and Housekeepers

Literally Putting Your House in Order

When the doctors told Mom to put her house in order, she did more than just plan her funeral. She also *literally* put her house in order.

Mom wanted to leave things as manageable as possible for Dad and the rest of us, so she kept her housecleaner in the loop regarding her health and future vision. She also started thinking about household items that needed to be updated or replaced.

Right away, she knew she wanted a new vacuum. So, as soon as she was out of the hospital and had the strength, we went straight to the vacuum store. She was set on buying a good one to leave behind for Dad and the people who would be keeping her legacy of a clean house.

I remember thinking, *This salesperson doesn't even realize how easy of a sale this is!*

Patty, you have always been a very important person in my life and you always will be.

—UNCLE KEVIN KEENAN

Video Interview

Documenting Her Story

Days after her diagnosis, Mom asked her youngest brother Kevin Keenan to do a video interview about her life. The summer before Mom's diagnosis, Kevin had videotaped a similar interview with their father, Jerry, where he asked questions about his childhood, his young adulthood, being married, raising children, his favorite activities, and more.

It was a way to document Grandpa's life not only in his own words but in his own voice. Video allows you to see *and* hear your loved one. You can capture someone's laughter, expressions, and emphasis.

Grandpa's video had some funny moments as well. For example, at one point the phone rang. Grandpa picked up the phone and answered it while the camera was still recording.

To help her prep for the interview, Kevin sent her a letter with some sample questions and topics they might cover. In the letter, he also reflected on the special brother-and-sister connections they had shared throughout life. It was a chance to remind her—and himself—about the good times, even while they processed this grave diagnosis.

Mom's desire to leave her legacy behind in her own words was important, so she mustered up the energy to do it. A memorable moment was when she cited how many times she had moved during childhood and young adulthood—only to never move again after she got married.

Here again, the video had some funny moments. The phone rang, and people can be seen moving around the house in the background. It was a good reminder that a video doesn't need to be "perfect" in order to be meaningful.

The interview brought Mom peace. She had documented her story in her own words. In her closing comments on the video, she emphasized how important family, faith, and friends were in her life.

The video is a legacy for generations. In the years since Mom's passing, we have added a welcomed new dimension to our family. My brother, Michael, and his wife, Julia, have two boys, Colin and Noah. In 2015, when the boys were four and six, Michael showed them the video. It allowed the boys to learn more about the grandmother they were not able to physically meet.

Part 2

living

with

cancer

Dear Patty,
I'm glad to hear you were able to get your
chemo treatment. You are such a wonder!
You have a positive attitude. You remind
me of my mother. She fought but never
complained. I hope you are feeling better soon.
We think of you and your family every day.

—AUNT KATHY KEENAN ON MOM'S
CARINGBRIDGE SITE

Appointments with Dawn

Looking for the Good News

For the entire journey of Mom's lung cancer treatments, our main medical point of contact was Dawn Aranguren, PA, of the Medical Oncology Evaluation Department at the Mayo Clinic. We attended many appointments with her throughout the cancer journey.

Mom and Dad were always together for the appointments, and usually another family member also attended to take notes, listen, and ask questions. We gathered this information to later post updates on CaringBridge.

I accompanied Mom and Dad to many of the appointments. My employer, Eagle's Flight, was extremely supportive and flexible, encouraging me to take care of myself and to spend my time wisely with my mother.

Even though we all showed it in different ways, nerves were high for everyone on appointment days. Each time we walked into that medical room with Dawn, we had to ready ourselves to hear about test results, look at lung scan comparisons on the computer, and discuss treatment options as well as potential side effects. Knowing that Mom's cancer was uncurable, we had to brace ourselves for bad news more often than not.

Thankfully, Dawn was always impeccably prepared and knowledgeable about Mom's case. The appointments would last from thirty to ninety minutes, and we never felt rushed.

We grew to have a close bond with Dawn, as we often shared intimate conversations at the appointments. We loved that the style and color of her hair was different almost every time we saw her, and we loved hearing about her annual Halloween party. We all shared a love for gardening and the changing of the seasons. Connecting personally softened the experience and helped calm our nerves.

I found going to the appointments beneficial in a number of ways. In the doctor's office, Mom was more honest about her symptoms, pains, and updates than she was in casual conversation with friends and family. Being at the appointments allowed me to hear directly and openly how she was doing.

It also allowed me to hear the medical information firsthand. Being present to hear Dawn's exact tone and choice of words helped me understand each phase of Mom's treatment.

More importantly, it gave me a clearer picture of the pending reality of one of my worst fears: Mom's death. This became even more crucial as Mom's resistance to the cancer decreased and her suffering increased.

In addition, being together at Mom's appointments helped us feel unified and connected. It was critical to my mental health and processing within the cancer journey.

After the appointments, we would go to a nearby restaurant to eat, decompress, talk, and decide who would be in charge of updating others with calls and the website. It was a comforting ritual and better for us than going our separate ways immediately.

During those meals, Dad would usually sum up the appointment by saying, "Well, the good news is . . ." He was always looking for the bright side as a way to cope.

Dear Patty and family,
This [website] is such a great way for us all to stay
in contact, while you conserve your energy for
your big fight. You are an inspiration to all who
know you and I learn from you constantly. Joe
and I think of you all the time and are grateful to
know that you are getting the best medical care
possible. I know you have a wide net of help and
assistance right now, but please let me know if I
can fill a gap. We love you very much!

—AUNT ANN KEENAN ON MOM'S
CARINGBRIDGE SITE

CaringBridge
How It Helped Us

After each appointment, one of us would post the notes and
updates on the CaringBridge electronic journal. People following
the site would then receive an email noting there was an update.
They could follow the email link to read the update and leave a
guestbook message if they chose to do so.

Some people wrote loving comments to Mom and our family. In particular, many shared notes of gratitude for how we were

sharing Mom's progress on the site. Seeing those messages was uplifting and energizing.

Other people just read the updates without leaving a comment, but this was encouraging too. CaringBridge kept a tally of the visits, and seeing those numbers gave us a boost.

I soon understood why Uncle Kevin encouraged me to start the CaringBridge site. There were so many benefits. It saved us time and energy. We didn't need countless calls and emails. All we had to do was type the latest updates once and then share it in this widespread and easily accessible way.

It also decreased confusion and inconvenience about the medical facts. On a practical level, it made it easier to inform people about the drugs Mom had been prescribed. Many of the names were hard to pronounce. It was easier to type them into the CaringBridge updates, rather than struggle to pronounce them in conversations.

On a deeper level, the CaringBridge site helped avoid rumors and misinformation. We didn't have to rely on other people using word of mouth to spread "updates" about Mom's treatment.

Thankfully, CaringBridge also conserved our emotional energy. I came to realize that sharing the latest update in person was draining. Sometimes, I could barely talk because of my tears. CaringBridge saved me from having to ask "What do you know so far?" or start the story from the beginning every time someone checked in. I could refer people to the site, and we could start the conversation from that point.

Mom loved the website. The journal entries about the appointments served as a good reference point and timeline for her. The photos we inserted captured her at different phases in her journey.

Best of all, the guestbook entries and visit tallies provided strong reassurance that people were thinking of us, praying, and sending loving words. She often referred to the guestbook entries as her support group. CaringBridge was a source of support for all of us, actually. It made Mom's journey feel more like a team effort than an individual endeavor. We didn't feel alone even in such uncharted times.

Sometimes, Mom would post comments on the site. She would voice gratitude or share fun news about special outings and the life she was still daring to live.

People started commenting how inspiring she was. For example, my cousin Katie Brekke posted on Mom's CaringBridge site, "You continue to be in our thoughts and prayers. Your attitude and strength are so inspiring."

Mom was humbled as well as touched. She wasn't trying to be inspiring. But it was a wonderful side effect of openly sharing and wanting others to learn through her story via the website.

Here is the December 2, 2005, CaringBridge entry written by Mom:

Dear Family and Friends,
Thank you for all your kind messages filled with hope. Now I have true empathy and compassion for everyone living with cancer. My horizons are broadened everyday as yours are, too. I have received a "chemo cap" which is so comfortable on my bare noggin. I'm wearing it all the time at home when it's just us here. It was a defining moment in my life and my family's when we learned I have lung cancer which is non-operable. Having my hair shaved off was bittersweet because for four days it was all over everything. It was hard to see myself in the mirror without hair. I look awful. So, this is part of this journey that many others have been on before me and I thank them for participating in research studies that have made it possible not to have nausea for

instance. As I read each of the messages in the guestbook, I pray for you. Merry Christmas!

Love, Patty

I used CaringBridge, too, to leave Mom messages filled with love and encouragement. Here's one from later that same month, on December 29, 2005:

Mom,

I always knew you were a teacher, but my big aha over the last month has been that teaching is your nature. Whether you are teaching me the Keenan Brunch recipe, teaching Dad how to fry eggs, or explaining the chemo side effects after Christmas brunch to a room full of family, including taking your wig off to expose your little bald head, you amaze me with your passion to teach. I am lucky to have been a student of yours all these years. In the same breath, I don't feel ready to "graduate." So, let's kick this!

Happy New Year! I am grateful you purchased Christmas cards at Hallmark December 26th on sale for next year. You will need them.

I love you,
Julie

Let's all try to get along.

—GRANDPA JERRY KEENAN

Kitchen Elves and Chemo Caps
The Gifts of Teamwork

It was incredible to see how many people added their talents and natural gifts to help support Mom and the family along this journey. The giving seemed to come naturally. That's because we created an open and appreciative atmosphere where people were welcome to contribute their gifts.

On March 20, 2006, Mom wrote a CaringBridge entry about the help she had received:

> *We have been on a life-changing detour and you have helped us on this journey. Now, maybe I can offer some tips in case you need them someday.*
>
> *I hope you'll have someone, like Doug, to take care of the medical paperwork. He saves me from this stress.*
>
> *I hope you'll have someone who will get the Caring-Bridge website going for you and keep updating it with current photos.*
>
> *I hope you have someone go with you when you visit with your doctor. They took better notes than Doug or I was capable of writing at the time for us to read and then post on this website.*

I thank God for the people who have made the chemo caps I wear everyday which keep my bare head warm.

Mom's post was informative and endearing. As a daughter, I'd like to share my perspective about the ways others lent their gifts to help.

Paperwork

As Mom mentioned, Dad was an advocate for her, handling the medical insurance paperwork. This included many phone calls with questions and follow-ups about coverage and payments.

He also led the task to confirm that her life insurance policies reflected her wishes. In addition, he initiated and scheduled meetings with their lawyer about her will, power of attorney, and health care directives. Both Mom and Dad attended the meetings, and together they updated and finalized documents.

I appreciate how Dad took the lead with these tasks. More importantly, I'm thankful that they were both proactive, addressing these matters while she still had the physical, mental, and emotional energy to focus on them. Knowing things were in order heightened her ability to rest and focus on her health.

Laundry

Doing the laundry maybe doesn't seem as important as handling medical and legal paperwork, but it was a significant area where Mom needed help. So, after thirty-five years of marriage, Dad learned how to do the laundry. That was a new skill he was willing to learn. (In contrast, his desire to learn much about cooking was low, but he still found ways to eat.)

Food

Family and friends often brought food. It was wonderful. Every time a meal arrived, it felt like a special gift and one less thing to worry about.

Mom's good friend Mary Ann Brandt coordinated a schedule with people willing to bring meals to Mom and Dad. Mary Ann lovingly referred to this group as the Kitchen Elves. She explained how it worked: "CaringBridge was the touchstone for finding the elves. Your mom candidly told me that although she was hungry and still interested in eating, she had neither the energy nor the interest in menu prep or cooking, so we did a Monday/Wednesday/Friday delivery."

Visits and Fun Outings
Whenever Mom had energy, she welcomed family and friends' visits, and she enjoyed going on outings. She loved getting manicures and pedicures, going to gardens, and sharing meals with loved ones. Her appetite for food was better when she was with others. Staying in touch and sharing lighthearted times was of great value.

I am grateful Mom felt supported through this strong team of loved ones.

Pronounce often and with great confidence the names of Jesus, Mary and Joseph. Their names bring peace, love, health, blessings, majesty, glory, admiration, joy, happiness, and veneration. Their holy names are a blessing to angels and men, and a terror to demons. Christians should always have the names of Jesus, Mary and Joseph in their hearts and on their lips.

—BLESSED BARTOLO LONGO

Prayer
The Glue That Kept Us Going

It might be hard to know how to help a family during a health crisis. Someone once said to my uncle Kevin, "I'll pray for you—it's the least I can do." To which Kevin responded, "It's the *best* you can do."

Mom would agree. Many times, she felt the loving power of prayers.

Mom first developed her prayer life at home as a child. She enjoyed her Catholic school education. Throughout her life, she had routines of going to Sunday Mass, honoring holy days of obligation, prioritizing attendance at sacraments for loved ones, and saying the rosary. She prayed everywhere she went. There were rosaries in her car and purses, and prayer books on her bedside table. She always prayed with Michael and me at bedtime during our childhoods.

She turned to God in the good times and the tough times. She turned to God all the time. As she did dishes at the kitchen sink, I remember overhearing her saying "Jesus, Mary, Joseph" over and over. During a tornado, she kept praying the Our Father out loud as she huddled us kids under an old leather chair, protecting us from a window crashing in.

During her cancer journey, we often asked for prayers in the CaringBridge posts. Shortly after many of the postings, especially a big update, she would tell me, "I can feel the power of the prayers already."

The spiritual support of the prayers buoyed us all—more than we even realized. Digesting the news from each doctor appointment was challenging. It was a blessing to know we had prayers uplifting us.

We also received prayer shawls during the cancer journey. Creating beautiful handknit prayer shawls is a heartfelt ministry for some churches and organizations. While the knitters create the shawls, they pray for the recipients.

Mom was often cold, due to losing her hair and weight, so the shawls warmed her body. In turn, they warmed her soul. Knowing each stitch was prayerfully made with love, and seeing Mom symbolically wrapped in prayer, was comforting.

My parents welcomed their parish priest every time he visited. Mom was not strong enough to attend Mass at certain times, so their priest visited to bless her, pray, and offer Communion.

Prayer was the glue of Mom's life before the illness and a bonding force during it. Now from heaven, she encourages her loved ones to be open so that we may heighten our own prayer lives.

As for my personal prayer life, I enjoy going to Sunday Mass and praying daily. I appreciate the foundation of prayer my parents and my Catholic education instilled in me.

During Mom's cancer journey and my grief journey, I often cried during Mass. Emotions would be released as I felt God's presence. Prayer was a vehicle to remind myself that God was near and part of the journey with us.

Prayer gave me strength to do the things I felt worthy of my mother's life and final days. Prayer bolstered me to show up as my best self, even though it was one of the most trying times of my life. Prayer gave me the courage to ask others for their prayers in return.

Seize the moment! Remember all those women
on the 'Titanic' who waved off the dessert cart.

—ERMA BOMBECK

No Regrets

Making the Most of Our Time Together

That summer, Mom and I saw this Erma Bombeck quote on a
set of napkins in a boutique. The napkins also featured a photo
of women wearing 1960s-style floral dresses as they laughed and
kidded around at a buffet. We bought the napkins. Although we
didn't know it on that day at the boutique, we would later use
them at the house when Mom was in hospice. The napkins set
a fun tone and were an encouraging nudge to make the most of
the time.

I believe time is our most precious commodity in life. And
time takes on even greater significance when someone you des-
perately love is leaving. It's time you can never get back.

In the early phase of Mom's cancer journey, I made a pact
with myself to make the most of my time with her so I would
have no regrets if (realistically, when) she died. That pact was a
strong driver in my behavior.

As mentioned earlier, I attended the majority of the Mayo
appointments with Mom and Dad. In order to make that happen, I had to manage my workload at my job. I took deliberate

steps to make sure my tasks were done in advance or could be covered while I was out of the office. Often, I was racing to get things done at the office before heading to the appointment, but it was all worth it.

I was also intentional about doing my best to focus on work when I was in the office and focus on Mom's health whenever I was at the appointments. I found mixing the two—thinking about her appointments at work or thinking about work when I was at Mayo—was too much of a clash. I mentally compartmentalized as much as I could to be strong and present in both situations.

Many times throughout Mom's journey, I reevaluated what I could handle. While I did not drop my whole life to take care of everything for her, I did make some value-based decisions on what "no regrets" meant to me.

This isn't to say that someone who doesn't go to a majority— or any—of their loved one's appointments would have regrets. Regrets are personal. We each have different needs, desires, work obligations, and so on.

I knew that the things I wanted to experience with Mom were different than other people's desires. Respecting ourselves as well as others throughout these trying circumstances can be challenging yet worth the effort.

What's important is to be intentional with how you use this precious time—and how you want to be able to look back on it someday.

No regrets.

If you follow your bliss, doors will open for you that wouldn't have opened for anyone else.

—JOSEPH CAMPBELL

Choosing Your Mindset
The Silver Lining

There are many ups and downs in life. Cancer adds another dimension.

One day, life was feeling heavy. On top of Mom's cancer, I had recently suffered a miscarriage, which left me feeling sad and frustrated. I had an especially emotional phone call with Mom, who was in good spirits in contrast to mine.

"I am so upset you have cancer!" I raged. "Don't you ever get upset that you have lung cancer? I don't know how you can be so upbeat, talking about who you're having lunch with today!"

Immediately, I realized I did not want to speak to my mother that way. Of all people, why was I taking my emotional tantrum out on her?

Before I could say another word, she replied, "When I received the diagnosis, at first, I was very sad. A few days later, I was able to move my mindset: *I am living with cancer.* I am still living. Cancer is not everything in my life. And that's how I stay upbeat. It's a way of thinking."

It calmed me down. I tried to adopt that same mindset as well as possible. Upon reflection, I am aware she decided—dared—to live when many others would have died in spirit long before they died physically.

She was an expert on finding silver linings in life.

I am making new friends even while I'm having chemo!

—MY MOM, PATTY JOHNSON

Formal and Informal
Support Groups

We received and came across many flyers with information about cancer support groups. Mom didn't want to join any ongoing groups. I'm not sure why. I know they're a source of strength and assurance for many people.

Even though Mom wasn't interested in joining a formal support group, I myself found support groups helpful in my journey as a family member. It was helpful to process my feelings in a supportive environment with people who could relate to my situation yet were removed from it. It allowed me to show up much stronger, and more consistently for my family.

Here again, it's good to point out that what worked for me might not work for everyone. We all process our situations differently. We all need to find what works for each of us.

While she didn't join formal groups, Mom already had many informal "support groups" she had fostered throughout her life. I'm grateful for the value she had placed on building relationships, being involved in the community, and taking interest in people's lives *before* she was diagnosed. All this effort and support boomeranged back to her when she needed it the most. Thus, she gave and received support in countless ways.

In a broad sense, her immediate family and extended family were of course support groups, as were her close friends and neighbors. But in addition to these expected sources, she also found informal or occasional support through other avenues.

Shopping Trips

"Rev up—we have to go shopping!" Mom often announced to me early mornings on weekends. She loved to shop at the mall.

A big part of the shopping experience was stopping to talk with other shoppers and salespeople. Grandpa Keenan would joke that Mom would stop every twenty feet to talk. She knew lots of people in the community, and she recognized them even if years had passed since their last visit. She'd always say hello.

In many ways, being out and about at the mall was like a support group. Just like finding a great deal, finding a unique and timely connection unexpectedly at the mall was a treasure.

Exchanges with Strangers

The mall wasn't the only place that gave Mom a chance to interact with other people. She was the type of person who could start a conversation with a stranger in an elevator and leave seconds later as friends. Whether she was at the hospital having chemo or sitting at a picnic table for a community event, she was sharing, listening, and enjoying connections with anyone near her.

Phone Calls

At the time, connecting in person was wonderful, but connecting over the phone was the next best thing. A ritual Mom and I shared for years in my adult life was talking on the phone most mornings for a few minutes. Conversations revolved around topics such as the weather, health, family and friends, news, food, schedules, and gardens.

During her cancer journey, this daily call gave her an easy outlet to discuss her symptoms. We would talk about how they were impacting her, whether they were known side effects or something unexpected, and whether they required doctor visits. Even if we only chatted for a short time, this daily call was a way for her to receive support and guidance—and a way for me to stay involved in her journey.

Church Services

With faith being the center of her life, going to Mass was a source of strength for Mom and a time to connect with others. While she had cancer, her priest was attentive to her religious needs. He often stopped by the house to give a blessing and pray with her.

Receiving Medical Care

Whether in Rochester or Mankato, Mom used her medical appointments and treatments as chances to energize her extroverted side. She appreciated all the medical personnel she interacted with, and she enjoyed meeting other patients undergoing treatments. In some cases, new friendships formed. She found ways for her personality to shine, even with a grave diagnosis.

Community Connections

Mom had always been active in the Mankato community, and she did her best to stay connected even during her cancer journey. She loved attending casual events with neighbors as well as community events such as concerts and the Relay For Life.

The Lake Home

Many special connections happened at my parents' lake home. My parents purchased lakefront property in northern Minnesota and had a lake home built in 1981. Ever since then, it has been a place for great relaxation, connections with nature, and memorable times with family and friends.

The lake home is a retreat for our family, a place where we spend cherished time together. We enjoy nature, delight in seeing animals and hearing the calls of the loons, eat home-cooked meals together, play games, take walks and boat rides, and more.

During Mom's cancer journey, being at our lake home was a form of support for her, as was her bond with the lake community. As you will see throughout the book, we have special memories of Mom at the lake home, and our lake neighbors do too. To this day, people often reminisce about times they fondly remember with her.

Class Reunions

Reconnecting with high school and college classmates through reunions was a highlight for Mom. Because she had stayed in touch with classmates over the years, many of them were able to offer prayer, support, gifts, and visits while she had cancer. Those were special connections for Mom.

Support through the Internet

As mentioned earlier in the book, the CaringBridge site was a major form of support for Mom and us all. My March 2, 2006, entry to all the readers touched on this:

> *Thanks for checking on things through the website. I never expected this website to be such a source of support, encouragement, faith and love for all of us as we journey through Mom's cancer. I am so thankful Kevin Keenan suggested we use CaringBridge to document accurate details of Mom's health. It is a true electronic support group. We treasure the guestbook entries.*

As you can see, Mom had many informal but deeply meaningful support groups in her life. In addition, I valued formal support groups. But again, it's important to emphasize that what worked for us may not work for you. Here—and throughout the entire book—I offer our experiences as inspiration for you to reflect upon your or your loved one's own connections, personality, and needs during life.

You have wings. Learn to use them and fly.

—RUMI

WINGS

Gifts and Support Uplifting Me

Friends were a source of love and support to my mindset and approach to Mom's journey. I was blessed to be in a spiritual friendship group that played an important role, especially during this emotional and trying time.

Our group was called Women In Nurturing Group for the Soul, or WINGS. It consisted of three soul sisters: Janae Bower, Sara George, and me. Over the years, we developed and evolved many rituals and goals to help us stay deeply connected, grow in our faith, and encourage each other. Having a formal commitment to the group gave us all the gifts of accountability, abundance, and personal transformation.

When Mom's cancer journey began, Janae and Sara must have made a pact to treat me extra special with actual gifts to show their love and support. On a regular basis, sweet gifts would appear: flowers, manicure gift certificates, an inspirational book, and restaurant gift cards to use with Justin. I joked that they must have set me up as a "project" on their calendars, with reminders popping up to do something for me on a recurring basis.

The gifts were always a treat to receive, and I truly valued the thought and message behind them. Whether big or small, gifts are a love language Mom and I shared. We understood how gifts symbolize comfort, love, and support.

Mom loved the attention, too, as Janae and Sara sent her some gifts as well. But most of all, Mom loved knowing I had good friends who would help me after she was gone. She was supportive of these friendships, knowing they bolstered my ability to handle all that was happening.

The WINGS group was also a great sounding board for decisions in my life. Janae and Sara supported, suggested, questioned, and provided insights.

During Mom's journey, her health often seemed like a wild card in my life. At any given time, I knew her health could change, and I would need to adjust my schedule to be helpful and present to her. It was important to me, yet it felt so overwhelming.

WINGS was able to help me hone in on my major priorities. Together, we created pearls of wisdom to live by during the trying times:

- Prayer helps.
- Trust in God's plan.
- Surround yourself with positive energy.
- Bump up self-care that is calming and nurturing.
- Let some ideas go. Not everything needs to be implemented right now.

When I was scrambling and trying to balance my own life with being there for Mom's, the WINGS wisdom gave me perspective. For example, when I worried about finding time and energy to have dinner guests and throw a party, the WINGS insight helped me let those ideas go so I could focus on self-care instead.

WINGS was a rare and precious gift in my life. I am deeply grateful for Janae and Sara in the countless ways they loved and supported me through the life-changing experience of Mom's journey.

Strange as it may sound, we can choose joy.
Two people can be part of the same event, but
one may choose to live it quite differently
than the other. One may choose to trust that
what happened, painful as it may be, holds a
promise. The other may choose despair and
be destroyed by it. What makes us human is
precisely this freedom of choice.

—HENRI J. M. NOUWEN

The Power of Appearance
Looking Put-Together Is a Choice

When Mom was in college, someone looked at her dorm room closet and said, "Are those *all* the clothes you have?" Prior to that comment, it never occurred to Mom that she didn't have many clothes.

After college, when she finally had money to spend, she often went shopping for clothing. She took pride in looking sharp, and she enjoyed planning her outfits for events.

Mom understood that looking put-together is important. Regardless of size and gender, how you look on the outside can say so much about how you feel on the inside.

Mom still held to these beliefs even during her cancer journey. As her weight fluctuated and sizes changed, she made a point to purchase clothing that was fit and fashionable. She even joked in the doctor's office how shopping was a form of yoga—lots of stretching and reaching. She also appreciated receiving chemo caps that kept her bald head warm as well as stylish.

It was about so much more than just clothes. Looking good and feeling good went hand in hand for Mom. It's an example of how she was a model of living in the present moment with hope. Even though she was facing incurable cancer, she dared to *live*. As part of that, she enjoyed looking beautiful in fresh and flattering fashions in her size.

At the same time, Mom was realistic about where her cancer journey would ultimately lead her. She had a practical mindset of wanting her clothing to be used and enjoyed by others. She downsized her closets, giving away any clothing and shoes she no longer wore. She gave me ideas on where and how the rest of her clothing could be distributed after her death as well.

She was specific, too, about what she wanted to wear in her casket. She selected a royal blue dress. The dress was not only beautiful; it also carried special memories. She had worn the dress at Justin and my wedding, along with a ring with a blue stone from Grandma Johnson's collection that matched the dress perfectly.

Mom was a teacher at heart. By taking care of her appearance, she taught me the importance of looking as put-together and sharp as possible too. We loved shopping for clothing together, especially during sales. She always encouraged me to look my best, even in trying times. She delighted in seeing me in fashionable, well-fitting outfits. It was a perk in her day, even when she was not feeling good physically.

When the twists and turns of the cancer journey demanded so much of our energy and time, something as simple as wearing comfortable, fun clothing affirmed our resolve. Dressing nicely was a form of self-care that lifted our spirits in the face of the terminal illness.

*They learned that the deepest stories are
those that we give one another, that the very
act of telling, listening, giving and receiving
can form a bridge from one heart to another.*

—ELLEN KORT

Contact Lists

How Many Address Books Do You Have?

Of course, Mom understood who was who in her life, but I couldn't keep everyone straight. She had two or three hand-written address books, photocopied typed address lists for book club members and neighbors, a few lists for college and high school reunion folks, and other miscellaneous notes with contact information. Mom knew who had moved, divorced, died, and so on.

I eventually realized that we needed to take the time and effort to compile these various contact lists into one up-to-date, user-friendly master list. As soon as I mentioned the idea to Mom, she was eager to get started.

So, we took on the project of combining it all into one Excel spreadsheet. It contained all her contacts, with columns for addresses, phone numbers, and details about the connections (e.g., someone from church, a neighbor, Dad's cousin, etc.).

As we worked on the project, we both knew its importance and purpose. At some point, the family would use this list to gather people for last goodbyes, inform people of her funeral, send thank-you notes, and more. We also noted that it would serve as a Christmas card list for Dad, which was a somewhat brighter reason.

I still have a printed working draft of the list with Mom's notes on it. Always a teacher, she corrected the spelling of names and updated information.

In retrospect, I get a sense that Mom enjoyed this project and was proud of completing it. She wanted to leave things in order as a service to her family and friends.

I'm grateful for the time we spent compiling the list when we both had the energy and emotional stability to do so. I do wonder, though: how long was she ready to create the list before I was ready?

In order to be remembered, leave nothing behind but goodness.

—MESSAGE FROM YOGI TEA

Endowment
Gifting Her Love of Education and Spirituality

As another part of "getting her house in order," Mom began the process of setting up an endowment fund. According to Tim Smith on the Investopedia website, "an endowment is a donation of money or property to a non-profit organization, which uses the resulting investment income for a specific purpose. . . . Most endowments are designed to keep the principal amount intact while using the investment income for charitable efforts."

Mom first became inspired by the endowment idea during visits with her dear friend Mary Ann Brandt. As former Catholic school teachers, Mom and Mary Ann both recognized how budgets were tight in the local school system. They felt strongly about the importance of funding this spiritual development.

Through continuing conversations with Mary Ann and Dad, Mom took steps to set up the Patricia and Douglas Johnson Religious and Spiritual Endowment Fund for the Mankato Loyola Catholic School. Thanks to Dad's diligence, the lawyer's legalese, input from the family, and Mom and Mary Ann's proofreading, a document was created to detail exactly how she wanted the endowment funds to support staff and student spiritual development.

Mom and Dad started the first donations with matched funds from Prudential, Dad's former employer. My brother, Michael, and his wife, Julia, donated to it as a Christmas gift. With it, they included a heartfelt letter on the difference Mom had made as a substitute teacher all those years.

Mom and I had several conversations about her intentions with the endowment. I was relieved her wishes were so clearly stated in the legal document. I knew that we, as a family, would be able to carry out her intentions to the letter. We wouldn't find ourselves with interpretation issues or uncertainty.

The foundation was set. As it would turn out, more pieces of the endowment would come together shortly before—and after—Mom's passing.

When Einstein gave thanks, he thought about why he was grateful. When you think about the reason why you're grateful for a particular thing, person, or situation, you will feel gratitude more deeply.

—RHONDA BYRNE

Greeting Cards and Tributes
Expressing Love and Attention

I love greeting cards. I love shopping at Hallmark. Hunting for the perfect card to give for a specific reason is one of my great joys in life. I love adding handwritten notes to cards, too. They emphasize and reiterate what I try to say in my actions and spoken words.

I sent many cards to Mom throughout her life. She looked forward to the daily mail, and she appreciated whenever someone took the time to send a greeting. In addition to cards from me, she received many cards from others over the course of her cancer journey. Each one was a little gift to her soul.

Mom also sent me many beautiful cards. They were always fun to receive. To this day, I enjoy looking back on the personal notes she added. Often the notes contained "Thank you" and "I love you." These messages are so meaningful to see in her handwriting now.

During Mom's cancer journey, I decided to send her a card with a handwritten tribute to her. It seemed fitting. Our relationship was very encouraging and filled with gratitude. She was my greatest cheerleader. In particular, she often told me I was a "natural" at this or that. And so I used that concept in my tribute to her.

> *You're a natural mother…*
> 1. *You listen.*
> 2. *You congratulate.*
> 3. *You do what you say you will do.*
> 4. *You remember.*
> 5. *You comfort.*
> 6. *You make time for others.*
> 7. *You are true to yourself.*
> 8. *You wish only the best for others.*
> 9. *You are consistent in being yourself.*
> 10. *You give compliments.*

Whether you write a ten-point tribute or just a quick "Love you," cards can be a wonderful way to express your love. Everyone's way of expression is unique. The important part is that we find a way to communicate our feelings in our own ways. Greeting cards can help us do just that.

I feel blessed that Mom created an atmosphere that honored the various ways people expressed themselves. She did not pass judgment and enjoyed receiving. Often the greatest gifts she gave were her genuine sense of amazement and gratefulness when she received a gift—even one as simple as a card in the mail.

It feels so incredible to give a gift to someone when you know they will savor and appreciate the gesture.

"Love" to me is appreciation to such a degree
that it fills my heart to bursting and overflows.

—LOUISE HAY

Professional Photographs

Functional Keepsakes

In 2006, my parents had a professional portrait taken of themselves as a couple for their church directory. The photo captured them well. They went the extra step to have their individual portraits taken as well. As gifts, they made prints of their joint and individual photos, Mom was happy to include their joint photo in their Christmas cards.

It's special to have this portrait of my parents. I especially appreciate it, seeing as it was the last time they were photographed together professionally.

A good photo is a treasure. More and more, I understand the importance of having high-quality portraits taken consistently in life, especially as we age. Getting your portrait taken on a regular basis is an amazing way to reflect on how your looks—and fashions—change.

Mom's individual portrait was beautiful. She looked wonderful, even though she was well into her cancer journey at the time. Having taken many of our own snapshots during her journey, we were aware that Mom photographed better in certain phases than others, due to differences in her hair, wigs, chemo caps, weight, coloring, and strength.

Because Mom's portrait was so great, I began to think ahead . . . It's customary to submit a photograph with an obituary. I knew this portrait would be perfect. Therefore, I called Lifetouch, the photography company, and explained that we foresaw using Mom's portrait for her funeral documents. They graciously touched up the color, sent a digital copy in a format that would work well for the newspaper, and sent some extra prints as well.

It might sound morbid to pick a photo for your mother's obituary while she's still alive. It also might sound hopeless and defeated. But honestly, I did it out of great love for her as well as myself.

Mom's cancer was uncurable. As hard as that was to face, and as much as I grieved during her journey, I knew the grief and pain would be even rawer in the hours and days after she died. So, anything I could do in advance—even something as "simple" as preparing the obituary photo—would be helpful.

As Oprah Winfrey says, "Love is in the details." Planning ahead allowed me to put love and attention into the details of the reality that stood before us, while still holding onto hope and living in the moment.

In the end, I am grateful that the photograph most used to memorialize Mom shows her true beauty and love in her eyes.

What if I made a book for my mother that shared memories of my childhood and growing up from my perspective as an adult? In effect, I would create a "baby book in reverse."

—JESSIE CHAPMAN

Baby Book in Reverse

Capturing Memories Growing Up

For my birthday, January 7, 2007, my lifelong close friend, Nancy Gnos, gave me the book *For My Mother* by Jessie Chapman. It's a keepsake book full of prompts to record special memories and messages for your mother. There's a range of topics, from "My favorite place in our home was . . ." to "The traits I'm most grateful to have inherited from you are . . ."

Along with the book, Nancy gave me a challenge, saying, "I figure you have time to have this ready for your mom as a Mother's Day gift." Having that timeline really helped me. I got to work.

As I made my way through the book, I poured out my heart. I added photos. I was honest about the good, the bad, and the ugly. I laughed and sobbed.

Through the experience, an aha moment came over me: I had been living with the fear of "But Mom doesn't know how much I love her . . ." ever since hearing the awful news of her diagnosis. Somehow, working on the book cleansed that fear. With my feelings there in writing, she would *know* the depth of my love. Freed from that fear, I could live more in the moment with her and cater to her ever-changing needs.

I gave the book to Mom that Mother's Day. She loved it and read it all.

I still have the book as a keepsake. It's a reminder of her aliveness and how well she lived what she believed. I'm grateful I wrote it when she was still alive. I would have written it differently after her death.

I do wonder, though: Was the book a greater gift to Mom or to me?

Will you still need me, will you still feed me,
when I'm sixty-four?

—JOHN LENNON AND PAUL MCCARTNEY

Sixty-Four Cards, Sixty-Four Messages
A Birthday Tribute

Birthdays have always been a cause for celebration in our family—
and they took on new meaning with a terminal cancer diagnosis.

The Beatles song "When I'm 64" was an uplifting touch
to Mom's sixty-fourth birthday on April 18, 2007. Around her
birthday time, she frequently played the song and had the words
typed up so she could sing along. I can still picture her swaying
back and forth and bouncing as she sang. She kept looking for
ways to be goofy and fun, which helped all of us. On her actual
birthday, Mom even sang the song on a message to her sister
Nora's answering machine. Nora would go on to keep the message until that machine broke.

The way she embraced the song was just one example of
how she continued to choose joy throughout her cancer journey.
Instead of focusing on how she might not have any more birthdays, she treasured her sixty-fourth year.

For her birthday gift, I made sixty-four greeting cards for
Mom. On the front of each was a photo of Mom I knew she liked.
Each card was blank inside but included a *You're IT!* bookmark,

a product Janae Bower created to go along with her *You're IT!* book. The bookmark featured a lovely quote from Janae: "Some people touch our lives briefly, and we change for the better. Others touch our lives deeply, and we're never the same."

While making the cards, I thought about my love for Mom and how grateful I was for the special role she played in many lives. So when I gave them to her on her birthday, I suggested she use them to write personal notes to sixty-four people who made a difference in her life.

Even though she appreciated the gift, Mom didn't immediately jump into writing the notes. I think it might have been a daunting initiative for her at first. Plus, she had varying energy levels due to her cancer treatments.

Over the year, though, she did write and mail all the cards. She ordered her list of the sixty-four recipients based on when they had come into her life. Ordering her list became a unique way to reflect on the course of her life and the wonderful people she loved.

Just as filling out the *For My Mother* book allowed me to express my love, the cards allowed Mom to express hers. They were an element of completion on each relationship. Later, when she was in the final days of her life, she was at peace. When people came to visit, she could say "You came" and then go back to peaceful resting. She had already told them how much they mattered in the cards—and throughout her entire life.

I wonder if the recipients realized the cards were Mom's way of recognizing the role they played in her life as well as her way of saying goodbye.

The ego uses everything to lead us further into anxiety.
The Holy Spirit uses everything to lead us into inner peace.

—MARIANNE WILLIAMSON

Difficult Conversations

Time to Stop Driving

There were many transitions within Mom's cancer journey. Each stage included necessary conversations. Some were difficult. One of those conversations was about whether Mom needed to stop driving.

During the last year of Mom's life, Grandpa Keenan told me he was concerned about Mom's driving, due to the cancer treatment side effects. He thought it would be best if she stopped driving.

Despite the fact that he was losing his eyesight, Grandpa's words about her driving meant a lot. He was a retired Minnesota State Patrol trooper and had taught defensive driving trainings. It didn't take a trooper, however, to realize the time had come to talk with Mom about driving.

When these difficult conversations need to be addressed, hopefully the right person—a friend, child, or partner—emerges for the situation. In this case, I decided to step forward.

Like everything else in Mom's cancer journey, it was surreal. I could hardly believe I needed to have this particular conversation with her. I was nervous. How could I bring up the topic? I didn't want to say something alarming, such as, "We were all talking behind your back about how you've been scaring passengers when you drive."

Saying goodbye to driving would be a huge change for her, but it was a necessary one for her safety and for others'. I hoped she would understand and agree.

One day when just Mom and I were at home, I asked a broad question: "How's it going driving?" And then I listened.

To my surprise, she shared that she wasn't as comfortable driving as she used to be. She realized she had made a few uncharacteristic mistakes, including running a red light. At the same time, she was concerned about how she could still get places if she stopped driving. She did not want to be a burden, always needing to ask for rides.

Based on her candid response, our conversation evolved. We talked about how her health issues were happening outside anyone's control. That is, she couldn't control how the side effects impacted her. What she *could* control, though, was the choice to drive or not drive. In this same spirit, we also talked about worst-case scenarios. Because the decision to drive was in her control, we would all feel horrible if she kept driving and then got into an accident.

With the conversation flowing in the right direction, I took the next step. I told her that Grandpa had noticed her driving had changed and that we were all wondering if she could stop driving. There were a few jokes between us about how her driving *must* be bad if a nearly blind person was noticing it.

With some open communication, we reached the decision that she would stop driving. I was relieved, knowing we had gotten through the difficult conversation. Mom was relieved, too, knowing it was the right time for this choice.

We then talked with Dad. He supported the decision.

Mom felt comfortable about sharing the decision with others. And just like that, friends and family began offering rides. A silver lining was that riding with others gave her more chances for special conversations.

Most importantly, life kept going.

The goal is not just to create joy for ourselves but, as the Archbishop poetically phrased it, "to be a reservoir of joy, an oasis of peace, a pool of serenity that can ripple out to all those around you." As we will see, joy is in fact quite contagious. As is love, compassion, and generosity.

—HIS HOLINESS THE DALAI LAMA AND
ARCHBISHOP DESMOND TUTU
WITH DOUGLAS ABRAMS

Vision Boards
Creating Inspirational Collages

At our annual WINGS retreat in the winter of 2007, Janae, Sara, and I created individual vision boards to represent our hopes, dreams, focuses, and desires for the upcoming year.

Basically, a vision board is a collage of meaningful photos, magazine headlines, stickers, and other materials. They're easy to make, and everyone I know who has created one has been thrilled with the results, tangibly and mentally. I looked at my board every morning, and it proved to be extremely centering and uplifting in the midst of the many directions and passions of my life.

In particular, my vision board really helped me cope with Mom's journey. For example, I can still remember the day I driving to work, talking with Mom on the phone. She mentioned a Mayo Clinic appointment in the near future. It was the first I had heard this news.

Instinctively, I wanted to get uptight and defensive. I wanted to say, "Why didn't you tell me about the appointment? I need to see if I can leave work so I can be there with you!" But instead, the word *flexible* popped up as if on a movie screen in my head. I had put *flexible* on my vision board as a mindset I wanted to uphold.

And so I was able to sidestep the defensive act. Instead, I just made note of the date and time of the appointment.

I shared my board with Mom. It was a fun way to talk about my current focuses and dreams in life. Little did we know that Mom would create her own vision board when the time was right . . .

Part 3

considering

hospice

If ever there is a tomorrow when we're not together, there is something you must always remember. You are braver than you believe, stronger than you seem, and smarter than you think. But the most important thing is, even if we're apart, I'll always be with you.

—A. A. MILNE

The Whisper

Writing a Eulogy

It was late June 2008. I was cleaning a mirror in my living room. Suddenly, I received a whisper: *You need to do a eulogy.* It was a whisper in my head, but it felt like a lightning bolt and a thunder crash, as if God were right there in the room.

As I looked in the mirror, my initial reaction was complete fear and *no, no, no.* I felt the task was physically bigger than me. I didn't want to think about Mom dying, let alone think about me doing a eulogy at her funeral.

I had never considered delivering a eulogy. I assumed one of Mom's brothers would do it. Yet as I reflected on Mom's cancer journey, I realized that our immediate family—Dad, Michael and Julia, and Justin and me—were the ones most closely involved. Perhaps it made more sense if one of us did a eulogy.

I jotted a note to myself in the kitchen: "Do eulogy." That way, I wouldn't forget the idea, but I wouldn't have to think about it much more that day. I decided to sleep on it. When I woke up, the thought was still strong.

That day, I went for a walk around Lake Harriet in Minneapolis with my friend, Kirsten Hargreaves. I enjoyed walking outside, as it was a good way to exercise, enjoy nature, and mentally process things in my life. Over the course of our three-mile walk, Kirsten and I talked about the whisper. She encouraged me to do a eulogy, emphasizing what a gift and tribute it would be to Mom.

That weekend, Janae and I walked along the Mississippi River in Saint Paul. As she mentioned in the foreword, she just so happened to have the book *Women's Lives, Women's Legacies: Passing Your Beliefs and Blessings to Future Generations* by Rachael Freed with her that day. Without knowing about the whisper, she had brought me a book that would no doubt help me craft a eulogy as a tribute to Mom's legacy.

In time, I came to see the whisper as the inception of the eulogy idea. It was a personal decision mixed with divine guidance. This concept struck me when Justin and I went to the drive-in to see the movie *Inception* a few years later. The film focuses on the inception, or birth, of ideas. This can be especially powerful when we believe the idea comes from inside of us rather than was planted by another person.

In comparison, what if someone else had told me I needed to a eulogy? Perhaps my fears and resistance would have stayed strong, and I wouldn't have done it. Who knows? And what if I had not heard the whisper or listened to it? Would I have regretted not delivering a eulogy and honoring Mom's legacy?

As I explored the idea more seriously, I realized that wanting to do a eulogy and actually being able to deliver one are two different things. I was very concerned about being able to speak at such an emotional time and not just get up there and cry. This had always been my fear when it came to other funerals. It kept me from participating in my grandma Keenan's funeral in 2001.

To move past this fear of crying, I paid attention when other people delivered emotional messages. For example, I observed Father Jim Cassidy at the Church of Saint Joan of Arc, where I'm a member. Father Jim frequently shared touching stories during his homilies, and often his eyes glossed over or his voice trembled when he became emotional. I started to notice how he would stop for a moment, take a breath, maybe grip the pulpit, then carry on. He didn't let the fear of crying stop him from delivering these emotional stories, nor did he sob in front of everyone. I gleaned as much as possible from watching him and others.

When the time was right, I had a conversation with Mom about whether I could give a eulogy at her funeral. She whole-heartedly encouraged me to do it. Her support meant the world to me.

Gradually, ideas came to me that helped prepare, write, and deliver the eulogy. Plus, I started to envision—though most of the time through tears—myself delivering the eulogy. That built up my strength for the actual funeral. I'll discuss that experience later in the book.

I'm grateful for the whisper. It helped me realize it was truly my role to give a eulogy. My hope for you is that you can be open and quiet enough to hear the whispers in your life. They are custom-made just for you.

God, grant me the serenity to accept the things I cannot change,
Courage to change the things I can,
And wisdom to know the difference.

—REINHOLD NIEBUHR

Introducing the *H* Word

Learning about Hospice

Mom had been on her cancer journey since Halloween 2005. And then at the July 15, 2008, appointment with Mom's doctor, we learned that the chemo treatments were no longer effective. They would be discontinued.

This is when the word *hospice*—which I called the "*H* word"—was suggested for the first time.

Hospice is end-of-life care, when someone with a terminal illness stops treatments and focuses on quality of life in what is inevitably their final phase of life. But to me, it felt like a swear word. I didn't want Dawn, our trusted medical advisor, to say that word in reference to my mother—someone who I once thought would outlive us all.

During the nearly three years of Mom's journey, no one had ever spoken of hospice. No one had addressed the reality that she would someday run out of treatment options and need end-of-life care—even though we had known from the start that the cancer was terminal. Instead, we'd always focused on treatments, staying strong, holding onto hope, daring to live.

Now I was dumbfounded. How could we suddenly cheat on hope and give up by going into hospice? Would it had helped if we had discussed hospice earlier in the process, as we prepared to embark on this journey? I'm not sure. I just wanted her to live. I didn't want her to need hospice or even need to consider it.

We left the appointment not knowing what to do. All we knew was that a decision needed to be made sooner than later. Was it truly time for Mom to enter hospice?

It hit our family hard and put us into shock. So much so that we weren't comfortable mentioning hospice directly on CaringBridge, even though we had always been so open with other details and medical news. We didn't know how to process what hospice would mean for Mom, and we weren't ready to answer any questions about it.

At the same time, we knew we had to update people and convey the seriousness of that transitional time. Even though I couldn't bring myself to use the *H* word, it was still a heartbreaking post to write. Here's my post from July 16, the day after Mom's appointment.

Tuesday, July 15ᵗʰ Patty, Doug, Justin and I met with Dawn Aranguren, PA, in Mayo Clinic's Medical Oncology Evaluation Department in Rochester, MN.

Mom's been weaker lately due to chemo and she mentioned how people have been offering an arm to help her walk, to which Dawn responded that she is a "walking miracle." Dawn's been a critical piece of the miracle and we are so grateful she's been helping us since November 2005. We've developed a close relationship with Dawn and will be forever grateful. The continuity in service and level of care we received from Mayo has been incredible.

The CT scan showed that the lungs are unchanged and the fluid has not redeveloped. The spots on the liver have gotten bigger and multiplied. The liver is still functioning, but it has more disease than it did in the May scan. There are no spots on other organs. The backbone has 2 spots which cause back pain and she needs to avoid heavy lifting (i.e. no wood splitting with Dad or lugging heavy suitcases). Since the cancer has progressed, the chemo is not helping enough to be warranted and will be discontinued.

Status:

Vitals are good.

Weight is very low at 110lbs. Mom has set a goal of gaining 5lbs in the next month. It might be more realistic to maintain weight or gain 3, but she's striving for 5. She needs to beef up the protein (I know, nice pun). So, bring on the bacon, pizza, butter, eggs, milk, cottage cheese, protein shakes, Culver's Shakes, etc. Plus, thanks to Justin, she's fallen for Chubby Hubby, a Ben and Jerry's ice cream. She enjoys eating out and being with people. She finds she eats more when she's out at a restaurant.

Leg cramps have been bothersome, and she will continue medication.

Hair is growing back.

It's gotten harder to do basic things (i.e. cooking, driving) as she gets tired and the ongoing side effects of chemo have taken a toll. We are all coming to terms in admitting and recognizing what she can and cannot do.

August 12th will be the next appointment with Dawn.

Thanks for checking the website. Mom wanted me to make special note to recognize all the guestbook entries, letters, cards, meals, rides, calls, love, and prayers. They help to keep all of us positive. The time is precious. God bless you.

Of course, a few people who read my CaringBridge journal entry surmised that hospice was probably the next step. Those who had been through a similar dying process with a loved one could read between the lines. But just because they picked up on it didn't mean they were comfortable talking about it. The *H* word seemed to be a taboo topic for them too.

Not everyone was silent, though. Tim O'Regan, my friend and coworker in Guelph, Ontario, specifically called me and wished me courage. His mother had died of cancer, so he easily read into the seriousness of the situation. His call was treasured, and it helped me cope with my new reality.

Mom's next doctor's appointment was scheduled for August 13. We had a month to let the news settle, learn more about hospice, and start talking with some of our loved ones about Mom potentially entering this new phase.

Be joyful though you have considered all the facts.

—WENDELL BERRY

Joy Boards

Treasured Things, People, and Ideas

Mom, Dad, Justin, and I were at the lake home for about a week that July. When the guys went golfing one day, I asked Mom if she'd like to create her own vision board, like the one I had done with the WINGS group.

Mom got pumped up by the idea. She wanted to get started right away. At that time, she was extremely thin and she tired easily. So, paging through magazines and cutting out things that appealed to her was peaceful, calming, yet also exciting.

As she worked, I watched closely, hoping her vision board would reveal themes, words, and concepts that could help me describe my cherished mom. With the eulogy still on my mind, I shared with her that I knew her too well to encapsulate her into words, yet I would be trying to do just that in the coming weeks.

The images on her board were less about "vision," in the sense of life goals, and more about her most treasured things, people, and ideas. It reminded her of how full her life was and what she loved.

When she completed her board, she was "high on joy," with a visible lightness in her movements. It seemed fitting to rename it her "joy board."

Doris Erickson, our friend and lake neighbor, stopped by that day, and Mom showed her the joy board. Mom's board had a magazine clipping saying, "A home cooked meal is an act of love." That got her and Doris talking about cooking and traditions. It was something positive to share, and it kept them off the heavier subjects of how Mom felt physically.

I had not anticipated how happy creating a joy board would make Mom feel. It turned out to be a wonderful tool that added energy to her day and helped ease her pain and suffering.

It was another testament to her resolve to *live* with cancer, even when she was contemplating end-of-life care. She did not play the victim role. She was still daring to live and cherishing the joy in her life.

May your precious objects, with their histories and stories, clarify your identity and values, and deepen your relationships with those you love.

—RACHAEL FREED

Precious Objects
Beloved Belongings Chosen for Loved Ones

In Grandma Keenan's final days, Mom helped her go through her jewelry and decide who would receive the items. Mom personally gave the jewelry to each recipient after Grandma died. She saw how touched people were to own something beloved and chosen for them.

Once she began her own cancer journey, Mom knew she wanted to make a list of who would receive certain belongings after she died. In particular, she wanted to focus on her jewelry. She loved wearing jewelry. She had inherited some from her mother as well as from Dad's mother. Plus, she had quite a collection of her own.

Mom often said she wanted to go through her jewelry with me, so I could help her sort it out and decide who should get which piece. But I kept putting it off. At the time, she was still undergoing treatment. We were still hoping for a miracle of her beating the cancer or somehow living forever. And she was still wearing her jewelry, so I didn't see an urgent need.

But once we realized hospice might be the next phase, I finally agreed to go through the jewelry with Mom.

"Great!" she exclaimed. "I've wanted to do that since my diagnosis!"

We appointed a Saturday to go through jewelry. While Dad and Justin kept themselves busy and out of the way, Mom and I began by spreading pieces out on the bed. I'd never realized just how much jewelry she had. Once I saw the amount, I understood why she didn't want to sort through it alone. I was grateful to go through it all together. As we worked, she shared many stories about where pieces came from or who gave them to her.

Next, we made a list people who would receive jewelry. There was a system. Mom wanted to be sure to include Julia and me, her sisters, her sisters-in-law, her goddaughters, and her close friends. She didn't want to exclude someone within those special groups.

Then, we looked over the pieces to see which one fit each person's style or connection with Mom. As she made each decision, we put the jewelry and other items such as rosaries in a box or small bag labeled with the recipient's name.

There was great value in Mom being able to personally handpick these keepsakes for the cherished women in her life. I quickly realized I couldn't have done it for her. Even as I watched her, I couldn't help but see it from a different perspective. I found myself comparing the value, size, and significance of one piece versus another. Sometimes I would ask, "Is that fair?"

Each time, Mom would just respond with something like, "That's what I want to happen." She wasn't concerned about the monetary value of each item. Rather, she was purely focused on the sentimental value. Each choice was lovingly, specially made for that person.

After dinner that evening, Justin needed to drive back to our home in Minneapolis. I was staying the night in Mankato. As he and I said goodbye, he knew I was starting to feel the impact of the day. There wasn't much to say. It was just a new wave of sadness.

As soon as he left, Mom and I went back to finish up the jewelry. That's when it hit me: we were passing on her jewelry because soon she wouldn't be here to wear it anymore.

Oh, the tears. A deep pain emerged from the pit of my soul. Here I was with Mom, knowing our time was limited but not wanting it to ever end.

"I don't want you to die!" I cried to her. "I want you to keep wearing this jewelry and be alive."

She held me and consoled me. "I don't want to die either," she said. "But I accept that this is my life's course."

Amidst this sensitive moment between mother and daughter, Dad suddenly started calling my name loudly up the stairs. "Julie! Julie!" he kept hollering.

As I wiped away tears, Mom responded, "Yes, Doug?"

"Julie, Justin called from his car!" Dad urgently said. "He wants you to look outside over the cornfield!"

We had no idea what he was talking about. We went to the window and were amazed to see fireflies lighting up all over the cornfield. It was an incredible, breathtaking sight. One I had never seen in all the years I had grown up in that house—or anywhere else, for that matter. Justin knew they would be something to marvel at, even through my tears.

Witnessing this marvelous scene of a field of blinking lights, Mom and I were assured that beauty surrounded us. Her impending death weighed on our hearts, yet this was proof that there would be cheerful light in the darkest of times.

Back into the reality of life again—and with a chuckle about Dad's hollering during our tender moment—we wrapped things up. We put the jewelry away, made some notes about pieces she was still wearing but wanted to gift, then went about other things.

By the end, I was emotionally drained. The whole day had been such a surreal experience, but one I was glad to have shared with Mom.

In more secular times, philosophers from Aristotle to Jefferson have assumed "the pursuit of happiness" was a noble aspiration of civilized life. In our own age, while we accept there may be different approaches to achieving happiness, we agree that happiness and joy are precious fruits of a life well lived.

—WAYNE MULLER

A Life Remembered

Sharing and Recording Your Life Story

During Mom's cancer journey, she reflected on life and was honest about relationships and milestones. I sensed she didn't want to take her life story to the grave; she wanted to share it and have it documented in her own words as much as possible. There was a desire to recognize the wonderfulness of life as well as the hardships and challenging relationships.

In what turned out to be the last weeks of Mom's life, her friend Laura Turk offered to document some of her life story. Here's what Laura wrote in the introduction of some conversations she documented with Mom:

> *Patty and I have known one another for a number of years. However, neither of us would say we played a significant role*

in one another's lives. But when, by chance, we did meet, we always felt a genuine interest in each other. Thus, it was only natural that in seeing Patty on July 23, 2008, at a Moon Dogs baseball game, she wanted to share with me her recent prognosis and told me about the limited time she had left to live.

After setting up a time for a visit, I made a clear decision not to come to Patty with an agenda. We would let our time together evolve into whatever felt comfortable.

After our first visit, it became apparent that Patty wanted to share brief chapters of her life. The conversations were not in any chronological order but through random thoughts and questions.

We often paused, laughed and/or cried as we had an unspoken understanding of life through the eyes of a woman. Patty felt delighted by simply reminiscing about important times in her life and said over and over, "Oh, this is good."

I am honored and grateful to have had the opportunity to share these conversations and know Patty at a much deeper level.

Laura created a compilation of their discussions, which ranged from Mom reflecting about her name, moving in childhood, memories from high school and college, teaching, money, and relationships. Some of the discussion topics were based on suggestions from *Women's Lives, Women's Legacies*, which I had used to help inspire the eulogy.

Author Rachael Freed shares, "I want to be remembered and tell my life story in my words. In my truth." That was apparent in Mom's case. The sharing was honest and, at times, raw. Mom yearned to record her perspective, and it sometimes evolved into an emotional purge as she reflected on her entire life.

I realize this approach would not be for everyone. Some may prefer to die with feelings unrevealed and secrets intact. But for Mom, this experience released some lingering tension surrounding her journey. The authentic sharing attributed to preparing her for a peaceful death.

You do not become good by trying to be good, but by finding the goodness that is already within you, and allowing that goodness to emerge.

—ECKHART TOLLE

Mission, Vision, Values
Defining What Matters Most

During Mom's uncertain and ever-changing cancer journey, I did my best to stay balanced, healthy, and kind. I knew time was limited, and I wanted to make the most of it.

I was thankful that I had already worked with Janae's *Can't Live Without IT: A Do-it-Yourself & Step-by-Step Guide to Developing Your Personal Mission, Vision, and Values*. From this guide, I created my mission, vision, and values statements. Those statements were a great source of focus, strength, and clarity and a wonderful framework from which to create goals.

As I began working on the eulogy, I realized that perhaps Mom would benefit from creating a mission, vision, and values statement. If she shaped these ideas in her own words, perhaps I could incorporate them into the eulogy.

It might seem strange to initiate a mission, vision, and values exercise in the final phase of one's life. The word *vision* seems especially odd in this case. Ultimately, though, a vision statement isn't just a plan for the future. Rather, it spells out the roles a person plays in life and details how they show up—or dream of showing up—in those roles.

As eager as I was to have Mom create her statements, the plan never fully came to fruition. By the time I sat down with her and Dad to start working through Janae's guide, Mom's energy was waning, she had other things on her mind, and she wanted to spend time with me in other ways. So, she never completed her mission, vision, values statements.

However, we did complete an exercise where she selected her top ten values in life. I enjoyed seeing her selections, and I gained greater perspective when she prioritized each value from one to ten.

I encourage you and your loved one to consider creating mission, vision, and values statements. If we had been able to create Mom's statements, I know they would have been such a powerful way to keep her memory alive in our hearts and minds.

There is so much to learn from one another, especially when we clearly state what matters to us and then compare that to what matters to others. Also, knowing someone's mission, vision, and values allows us to even better support, honor, and cherish what they hold most dear. It provides great insights into people's priorities and loves in their final chapter of life on earth.

The better course of valor is to stop the cancer treatments and utilize the services of in-home hospice care.

—DAWN ARANGUREN, MOM'S
PHYSICIAN ASSISTANT

The Decision

Choosing to Enter Hospice

On August 12, 2008, we headed to Mom's appointment. Mom, Dad, Michael, and I listened as Dawn discussed hospice once again. The appointment was filled with a reality that was hard to face.

It was then that the decision was made to enroll Mom in hospice. Services would officially start on September 4, after an extended Labor Day weekend at the lake home.

It was such a complex decision. Feelings ranged from sadness, shock, confusion, denial, and surrender.

Actually, Mom seemed relieved. The more she learned about hospice, the more she was on board with it. She even got to the point of saying she was looking forward to it starting. After undergoing treatments and struggling with side effects for nearly three years, comfort care sounded appealing to her.

At the end of the appointment, Mom asked me to stay in the room with her and Dawn. Mom's latest scans had detected a cancerous lump in her breast as well as increased growth on her liver. The lung cancer had likely metastasized and spread, though perhaps the lump in her breast was a new form of primary cancer.

Always the teacher, Mom wanted to show me what a lump looks and feels like. I felt the lump. It was about the size of a ping-pong ball.

I looked at Dawn. "What will we do about this lump?"

Dawn slowly shook her head, looked me in the eye, and reminded me we were no longer pursuing any sort of cancer treatment.

It felt so counterintuitive and even countercultural to stop treatment on a disease. Even though Mom's cancer treatment were often grueling and often painful, it had provided a strong sense of "getting ahead" of the disease or "stalling" it.

But now we had reached a point where treatments were getting us nowhere. I had to reprogram my brain to see the benefits of letting Mom enjoy her remaining time in hospice.

I now have the luxury of reflecting back on our timeline. From the moment we learned that Mom's treatments were no longer effective, it took a month to finally choose to enroll her, and then it took another two weeks to finally begin services. Six weeks.

As you will learn in the coming pages, she was in hospice for thirteen days before she died.

In truth, the reason Mom had not been enrolled in hospice sooner was that no one else in the family wanted it or was even knowledgeable about hospice services. Her cancer journey had always been driven by hope, and we didn't immediately understand that hospice was a way to redefine hope and do what was best for Mom. In retrospect, the most loving decision would have been to begin hospice earlier, so she could have had more of the comfort care services longer.

We did her a disservice not starting sooner. We did not make the decision earlier because of our discomfort—unfortunately, causing her more discomfort. She was comfortable about starting hospice. As a family we were not ready to accept how her health was deteriorating to the point of needing hospice.

And again, I wonder if learning about hospice earlier in the journey would have helped us feel more comfortable and more willing to enroll sooner. We may have benefited from learning about hospice in the very beginning, when it could have been presented as one of many options within a long-range plan. Instead, we learned about it only when it was an immediate necessity—in effect, when it was the only option left.

I mention all this to encourage you to be open minded to hospice earlier in your loved one's process, as soon as no treatment options are available or desired. Hospice enables the final period of life to be fuller and richer. Generally, I don't hear anyone complaining about starting hospice "too early."

Keep in mind, too, that it takes time to get into the flow of hospice care, even once it officially begins. Beginning it days before death may not be enough time to fully experience its benefits. The sooner you begin it, the more comfort it can provide your loved one, family, and friends.

In the end, I am grateful for learning about hospice at least when we did and for making the right decision to enroll. I am left with a deep sense that everything went according to plan for Mom's life.

Life doesn't always work the way we'd like it to. If we had our way, it would be easier, consistently fair, and more fun. There'd be no pain and suffering, we wouldn't have to work, and we wouldn't have to die. We'd be happy all the time. Unfortunately, we don't get our way. We get reality instead. But reality is a great teacher. It helps us learn, although often slowly and painfully, some of life's most valuable lessons. One of them is this: the world will not devote itself to making us happy.

—HAL URBAN

Sharing the News

CaringBridge Post about Enrolling in Hospice

The day after the appointment, Michael posted the news on CaringBridge.

> *The family experienced an emotional meeting with Dawn yesterday at the Mayo Clinic. Patty's lung cancer has progressed to a level where further treatment poses more risks than benefits. Therefore, as Dawn said, the better course of*

valor is to stop the cancer treatments and utilize the services of in-home hospice care.

The hospice program will eventually provide a hospital bed in the home, along with pain management and medication. A medical professional will visit the home and go over some of the important end-of-life issues that need to be confronted. The hospice care will be arranged through the Mankato hospital.

Patty's condition no longer allows her to cook meals. Our wonderful friend Mary Ann Brandt has graciously agreed to help us coordinate meals for Patty and Doug. She will create a calendar system that will make sure the meals are spread out and delivered as needed. If you are able to help, please contact her. Because of the upcoming Labor Day holiday trip to the lake, we hope to start providing meals after Labor Day. Through Mary Ann's Irish hospitality and my father's German efficiency, we can provide nourishing meals to Patty.

In the near future, we will need volunteers to stay with Patty while Doug is away. The hospice staff will not perform 24-hour care. Please let us know if you are able to help.

In general, the lung cancer continues to spread throughout her body. It recently spread to her left breast, but there is a slight possibility it is the onset of breast cancer. The scans showed increased growth on the liver and in the lungs. Because Patty will no longer be receiving cancer treatment, she will not undergo more scans or bloodwork.

Dawn told us today that when she first met Patty two and a half years ago, she gave her six months to live. Patty has endured numerous rounds of chemo, several radiation sessions, countless painful side effects, and lost her hair three times. Through it all, she has been an inspiration and never complained. As we go through these trying days, we ask for your prayers and a continuation of the remarkable love we have felt over these past several years.

*Nothing to me feels as good as laughing
incredibly hard.*

—STEVE CARELL

Laughter and Joy
More Joy Boards and the Belly Laugh List

Can we smile and laugh? I asked myself in late August. I didn't
know what was appropriate or acceptable now that we were ready-
ing for hospice to begin after our extended Labor Day gathering.

But as I arrived at the lake home, I immediately learned that
Mom wanted joy and laughter to be part of her hospice journey.
One of the first things she said to me was, "I want to create more
joy boards! I have a pile of magazines on the loveseat to use."

Given the circumstances, I was surprised she wanted to
make more boards, but I went with it. As it turned out, it was
wonderful to see her so happy in the process of creating. I could
feel her vibration of joy. Her new boards revealed her intention
of being joyful, laughing, and loving. She clipped "Choose the
Happier Thought" from a magazine and made it the focus of one
of her boards.

Her boards gave me insight into her thoughts, mindsets,
and loves. They helped me know what she wanted at the present
moment and what I should encourage. It gave me a clue about
the tone she wanted to exude during her final weeks. Plus, the

boards and the time creating them with her added to the inspiration of what to include in the eulogy.

Because her joy boards focused so much on laughter, joy, and happiness, I decided to take steps to create an environment of those elements, even in the face of death. I asked her, "Who can really get you laughing?" A few days later, I sent a letter to the people she listed:

> *Recently, I asked Mom who really gets her laughing. She thought about it and gave me a short list.*
>
> *Guess what? You're on her laughter list.*
>
> *Now, I usually don't associate belly laughing with the last phase of life or a hospice activity. Yet the more I learn about hospice, the more I realize humor can be a big part of someone's journey at this point.*
>
> *One of Mom's top self-proclaimed focuses for her life right now is joy. She keeps emphasizing the desire to be happy, smiling and laughing. Since you are someone she identified as adding a lot of humor to her life, please continue to do that to help fulfill her goal of being joyful in this phase.*

I wonder if the letter impacted those people's behavior with Mom. She was alive only a couple of weeks from when they received it. I realize there wasn't much time for them to respond. Still, I'm grateful for the people on Mom's belly laugh list, and I'm grateful for the laughter I still share with them. With or without a serious illness, joy, happiness, and laughter are worth cherishing.

Take no revenge and cherish no grudge against your own people. You shall love your neighbor as yourself.

—LEVITICUS 19:18

Difficult Conversations
Leaving Nothing Unsaid

Mom and I loved having conversations together. Many were jovial, loving, and heartfelt. We did have disagreements and frustrations with each other throughout life, though, including while she had cancer. But we worked through them; we asked for and granted forgiveness.

We were eating at a café at one point during the last months of her life. I took the opportunity to ask if there was anything she needed to hear from me. In our precious time together, I wanted to be sure we were on the best of terms. Perhaps she was waiting for me to address some topic, whether positive or negative. Perhaps she was holding a grudge that I had never realized. I didn't want to leave anything unspoken, no matter how difficult it may have been to face.

Mom couldn't think of anything left unsaid between us. Instead, Mom seized the moment to discuss a separate topic: Dad's future once she was gone. Their marriage had been a good partnership of sharing love, tasks, and responsibilities. She knew he would enjoy having another partner for the rest of his life. She predicted that he would remarry, and she gave her blessing on that choice.

It helped to know her viewpoint, as different people have different ideas about remarriage. For instance, when Grandma was in hospice, she and Grandpa discussed how he would not remarry. They were in their eighties at time, which may have impacted their outlook, as compared to my parents'. Grandpa did go on to have a lady friend, and they shared many happy times together. But one of the first things he told her was he wasn't interested in getting married.

I'm grateful Mom opened up about her thoughts on Dad remarrying. Additionally, I'm grateful I asked if there was anything left unsaid between the two of us. Although it didn't lead to a difficult conversation, it could have. Still, I put it out there. It was a relief to give it air and space, so we could then continue living in the present.

Hospice is not about giving up hope. It's redefining it and looking for new ways to define hope. A lot of healing can happen at this time.

—FATHER JIM CASSIDY

Understanding and Acceptance

Transitioning into Hospice

From the moment we first heard the *H* word back in July, I tried to wrap my head around the concept of hospice care. While I understood it on a surface level, I struggled to truly grasp it on a deeper level. Something in me kept resisting the whole idea. I didn't want to understand what hospice *was*, let alone why my mother needed it.

Then, in August, days before Mom began hospice, a phone conversation with Father Jim Cassidy became a turning point in my life.

So many questions were running through my mind about hospice. Father Jim had the right words, the right timing, and the right tone. He didn't try to talk me into anything. Instead, he gently painted the picture of how hospice works, what I could expect, and how it could be good for both the patient and family.

It wasn't a long conversation, but for the first time, I found myself willing to *fully* understand hospice services and benefits.

I went from clueless to curious to calmed. It helped me embrace and support this phase of Mom's life.

I took notes so I could share some of the ideas with others in my August 25, 2008, CaringBridge post.

Thanks for all the wonderful website guestbook entries, cards, calls, and attention. We feel very blessed to have so much support and love surrounding us.

The hospice intake meeting will be September 4 in Mankato. Julia will be there with Mom and Dad and will send an update afterwards.

Based on how much Mom is talking about food and telling me how things taste, I think she's gaining weight, thanks to starting the weight gain medication and all the good food.

I spoke with Father Jim Cassidy, a chaplain at Allina Hospice as well as a fabulous priest at St. Joan of Arc Church. He shared many nuggets of wisdom with me. Here are some that gave me great peace moving into this hospice phase:

Hospice is not about giving up hope. It's redefining it and looking for new ways to define hope. A lot of healing can happen at this time.

Hospice is aggressive comfort care.

Keep the hospice services bundled by saying "yes" to it all. It's a Medicare benefit—she paid taxes all her life, so utilize the services.

People in the last phase of life on earth often live longer in hospice than without hospice.

There is not a right or wrong way to do this (no perfect book or thing to say). Every family is unique.

For loved ones, it is a good time to visit, but don't "set up the tent too early." Gauge the level of attentiveness we give her, based on what she needs.

The hospice team will "hold the lantern to the road." No one can completely predict the how or when.

For 13 months after the death, there is bereavement care for the family. Knowledge of this is often very comforting for the patient.

God bless you.

It's the Circle of Life, and it moves us all, through despair and hope, through faith and love, 'til we find our place on the path unwinding.

—*TIM RICE AND ELTON JOHN*

Life Keeps Circling

Pregnancy and Death

An example of the circle of life happened the last time Mom was at our lake home. It was Labor Day weekend. Michael and Julia shared with Mom, Dad, Justin, and me that Julia was pregnant. Everyone in the family was happy for Michael and Julia. This baby would be the first grandchild.

We didn't know it at the time, but Mom would be gone in less than two weeks.

The baby, Colin, would be born in April 2009.

Mom would have been an incredibly loving, nurturing, involved, and generous grandmother. It's heartbreaking that she wasn't able to be part of this child's life, nor a part of Noah's life, as he arrived in February 2011.

Of course, I sense she is spiritually with her grandchildren, and she still loves them.

But that's a different love.

My friends, if we tend to the things that are important in life, if we are right with those we love and behave in line with our faith, our lives will not be cursed with the aching, throb of unfulfilled business. Our words will always be sincere, our embraces will be tight. We will never wallow in the agony of 'I could have, I should have.' We can sleep in a storm. And when it's time, our good-byes will be complete.

—MITCH ALBOM

Letting Go

A Million Goodbyes

During that final time at the lake home together, Mom and I were sitting side by side on the front patio, gazing out at the lake.

In her big floppy hat, she said, "It's going faster than I thought."

"I know," I replied.

Neither of us cried in that moment. We just let the realization sink in, knowing our physical time together would be ending soon.

We were quiet, and we continued to look at the lake.

Part 4

hospice

Unlike other medical care, the focus of hospice care isn't to cure the underlying disease. The goal is to support the highest quality of life possible for whatever time remains.

—MAYO CLINIC

Starting Hospice

The Official Announcement

Mom officially began hospice on September 4. Although we had resisted the idea of hospice at first, we quickly realized that the process and services gave us structure and peace of mind.

Julia shared the news with friends and family on September 7:

On Thursday, September 4, Patty, Doug, friend Pat Matejcek, and daughter-in-law Julia Johnson met with home hospice representatives for the official admission to hospice care for Patty. Social worker Stephanie arrived first to go over the mission of hospice and arrange multidisciplinary services. Patty chose the following visits:

- *Social worker: monthly visit*
- *Primary care doctor: optional visits (most issues will be handled by the hospice nurse)*
- *Nurse: 2–3 times/wk*

- *Home health aides: 5 times/wk for assistance with self-care*
- *Chaplain (a Polish Catholic priest who has met the pope and Mother Teresa): visits to be determined. This will not replace support from Fr. Wilmot and St. Joseph the Worker Church, but supplement care for Patty.*
- *Bereavement counselor: options include family meetings, many different group offerings, and grief/ loss support for the family up to one year after death.*
- *Hospice volunteers: no scheduled visits for now. If Doug is gone and Patty needs someone to stay with her, they will first use the list of generous friends who have offered their time. Hospice volunteers will be backup options.*

The hospice admit nurse, Leah, then came for a visit that included a review of medications. Patty decided to remain on only two as-needed meds: one for pain and one for anxiety/improving breathing.

One very helpful accomplishment was ordering the needed equipment for the home to increase Patty's comfort level. The following will be delivered on Monday, September 8: hospital bed (to be set up in the dining room on first floor) with linen, over-the-bed table, baby monitor so Patty can ask for Doug if he is upstairs or outside, shower chair, two toilet risers, oxygen concentrator, and a wheelchair with bag for portable oxygen.

Both the social worker and nurse could not have been more gentle and perfectly suited to their jobs. We all very much appreciated their sensitivity to our needs.

The hospice team was a treasure—such passionate, loving, and remarkable people. They added a new dimension of support and knowledge to our circumstances.

In terms of emotional support, they were a breath of fresh air coming into the home. They were always willing to spend extra time with us, answer our questions, and help us understand the stages. They supported and affirmed our decision to create a loving, peaceful atmosphere around Mom and ourselves.

There was a beautiful partnership between our family and the hospice team. As things began, I was genuinely surprised to discover how much responsibility was in our hands as family and friends. Before understanding services, I had assumed the hospice staff would be at the house nearly full time to care for Mom.

But then reality sunk in. We learned that hospice staff would come to the house for thirty to ninety minutes a day. The bulk of the responsibility was placed on us as family and friends.

Throughout her life, when faced with intimidating or challenging experiences, Mom often said, "We need to rise to the occasion." Our team of family and friends had to be strong in our commitment to keep up with Mom's care. This was the ultimate in rising to the occasion. We were unsure how long Mom would live. We heard it could take days, weeks, or months.

Thanks to the hospice team, we received an abundance of just-in-time training. They were great at coaching, such as when they taught me how to administer morphine when Mom was in pain. We weren't completely on our own, of course. We knew we could always contact hospice staff via a nurse line, and they were always accommodating when we asked for assistance. The hospice team helped us provide comfort care to our dearest loved one in this time of great transition.

We did not know it at the time, but we were in the final days of her life.

Patty, a song from the musical Wicked *always reminds me of you. The song, "For Good," is beautiful and poignant. You have touched so many lives with your example of living a virtuous life. You have changed us all.*

—AUNT JUDY KEENAN ON MOM'S
CARINGBRIDGE SITE

Sharing a Song

Expressing Feelings through Music

The hospital bed was scheduled to be delivered soon, and Mom's oldest brother, Tom, and his wife, Judy, happened to be visiting at the house. Tom offered to help Dad prep the dining room by removing the table.

Meanwhile, Judy had a special conversation with Mom in the living room. Judy played the song "For Good" from the Broadway musical *Wicked*. She dedicated the song to Mom, as she had in a CaringBridge post a few weeks earlier.

Who can say if I've been changed for the better?
I do believe I have been changed for the better
And because I knew you . . .
Because I knew you . . .

Because I knew you
I have been changed for good.

In a loved one's last days, some people shy away from expressing themselves. Perhaps it's because they don't know what to say or can't find the words. Sharing a song is a beautiful way to convey feelings.

Music was a salve many times during hospice. It soothed our hearts, minds, and souls as we adjusted to our current reality. Laughter, tears, and dancing were the side effects of turning on a little music, depending on the song and the timing.

By playing that touching song for Mom, Judy shared her feelings openly, even in the midst of all the prep work for the bed delivery. Judy understood that time was limited; she knew there might never be a better moment. Now she can always take comfort in knowing that Mom knew how she felt.

I was in the house when Judy played the song for Mom. I knew the song well. It was an absolutely beautiful experience, and as grateful as I was for it, I found it was just too much to absorb emotionally.

I decided to help Dad and Tom in the dining room. As the music filled the whole house, I kept reflecting on how odd it all was: we were taking the table out of the dining room, knowing full well that Mom would be dead when the table returned.

Oh, how I ached.

And, at times, still do.

The fear of death follows from the fear of life. A man who lives fully is prepared to die at any time.

—CHRIS ROCK

Surrender

The Hospice Bed

Once the bed was set up on September 8, Mom got in and basically started letting go. A similar thing had happened eight years earlier, when Mom's mother was in hospice at home.

The bed symbolized both surrender and acceptance.

Mom was releasing more and more from this life in order to begin the next.

*Our fashion choices are a glimpse into
our soul and help bring our inner feelings
outward. Fashion can help mask or enhance
our truth. Plus, on a lighter note, it's fun to
say, "Girl, you look good!"*

—HOLLY LOCHER

New Nightgowns
Choice, Control, and Positivity

Mom always found strength in feeling good about her clothing. Knowing that she valued looking presentable, I thought it might be comforting for her to have some new Karen Neuburger–brand nightgowns. I picked out a few that were especially soft and beautiful.

Really, it wasn't about fashion. It was about choice. In what turned out to be her final days, Mom still had the power to choose to wear beautiful pajamas, to feel put together. As insignificant as it may seem, her clothing was something she could control in the midst of so many circumstances she couldn't. Even while lying in a bed during hospice, she made the choice to have a positive attitude, and feeling confident in what she was wearing only added to her outlook.

Even guests could sense the positivity Mom's appearance and clothing conveyed. Her sister Nora reflected on how visitors seemed as comforted by Mom's pretty nightgowns as she did.

A simple choice had a big impact.

NO is one of the smallest words in our language and is one of the most powerful inner process tools we have for maintaining our authenticity, health, and well-being. NO is a boundary-setting word. Setting appropriate boundaries is essential to living an authentic, self-realized life. When NO is felt as a heart/gut–based emotional imperative, and we say YES instead, the resulting stress can have a profoundly debilitating impact on the quality of our moment-to-moment life and physical health.

—HERB KEARSE

Energy Shifts

Staying within the Comforts of Home

Over the years, my parents led an active lifestyle. They regularly went to church, visited friends and family, dined at restaurants, traveled, hosted gatherings in their homes, attended community events, and more.

Even throughout her cancer journey, Mom stayed quite active. She knew how to work around the "down" days of her chemo side effects. She knew it was important to stay active because it enriched her positive attitude.

She was especially grateful for things she and Dad could do together. She often credited him for helping her get out of the house on the days when it would've been easy to stay on the couch.

Mom stayed active even into August, when we learned hospice was right around the corner. But when hospice started in September, there was a sudden, dramatic shift. Her energy quickly declined, especially as she surrendered to the hospital bed.

This shift was hard for us all to grasp, but it was especially hard for Dad. In those first days of hospice, he made plans as if both he and Mom would carry on with their calendar as normal: attending church, going on weekend getaways with friends, and so on.

From my perspective, though, I could tell that Mom was no longer eager to leave the house. I wasn't eager for her to leave either. Not only was her energy declining, so was her immune system.

When Dad made plans or asked Mom about upcoming activities, I'd try to help them navigate the moment. For instance, when Dad asked what Mass they should attend that weekend, I helped them realize it would be best for Mom to stay home and watch Mass on TV.

After navigating several of these moments, it finally hit me: maybe staying at home needed to be Mom's new normal.

I discussed this with Mom and Dad. I explained that given Mom's weakening state, perhaps it was best for her to stay home and preserve her energy. We wanted to make the most of this hospice time.

Together, they agreed it was best for Mom to stay home. It was a huge decision, and it made many other things black and white for both of them.

For Mom, the decision was a huge relief. She was ready for it—she realized she was physically incapable of keeping up the pace and lifestyle they had been living. Finding the energy to leave the bed, let alone the house, was difficult. She knew her time was drawing near.

For Dad, realizing Mom was staying home was a huge point of clarity. It was a tangible understanding he could act upon. He took out his calendar, got on the phone, and changed or declined activities, explaining that it was due to Mom's health.

I knew the decision would help us all get along more easily. I was grateful we had come to a common understanding together.

May you realize that the shape of your soul is unique, that you have a special destiny here, that behind the façade of your life there is something beautiful and eternal happening. May you learn to see yourself with the same delight, pride, and expectation with which God sees you in every moment.

—JOHN O'DONOHUE

Fulfilling Her Wish

Dying at Home

Mom was clear about her wish to die at home. It was a given, actually. I don't remember needing to have a big conversation about it. We all just knew. In 2001, her mother had died at home while in the hospice program. Thus, she had set the example.

For Mom, dying at home meant being surrounded by beauty, peacefulness, and people she lovingly trusted. Mom cherished the beauty of the home where she had lived most her life. She was surrounded by the colors and lighting she loved. She was comforted by the familiar sounds of the home, in contrast to the unfamiliar noises of a hospital. She could look out her windows to see her gardens flourishing and swaying in the light breezes.

Visitors, too, felt comfortable in her home. It allowed them to connect with her more easily. There was an air of tranquility at home.

If your loved one is at home during their final days, you have to trust your instincts about what will be comforting for them. It will be different for each individual. What might feel natural to one person might feel unnatural to another. If there's time, start a conversation with your loved one about the things that bring them comfort. Ask about scents, sounds, scenery, activities, and more.

After going through Mom's experience, I strongly believe it is a gift to enable a peaceful death at home. And thanks to the great deal of support we received from many loving hands, we were able to give Mom that gift, that last wish.

A wise being completely and totally embraces the reality, the inevitability, and the unpredictability of death.

—MICHAEL A. SINGER

Invitations and Boundaries

Setting Guidelines for Visitors

With every passing day of hospice, we realized that Mom's lifetime was more limited than we had hoped. Many friends and family were anxious to visit and say their final goodbyes.

But as visitors poured in, those of us in the immediate family could see how taxing it was on Mom and how long it took her to recover from each visit. Mom's social energy was declining.

Julia wrote a CaringBridge post sharing our thoughts and guidelines about visits.

> *A few tips for visitors:*
>
> *Please call Doug to schedule a good time. Note that it is increasingly difficult for Patty to talk on the phone.*
>
> *Short visits work best, 5-10 minutes or approximately 60 minutes if coming for a meal. Longer visits have depleted her energy for the next few days. Family arriving from out of town is always welcome, of course . . . Call Julia, Michael, Justin or Julie for any questions on helping with Patty's current level of function.*

> *Patty's appetite will be naturally tapering. Per the nurse, "her body knows what she needs," so it's OK to offer food/drink, but don't force it, as it may make her sick.*
>
> *Don't call 911. Patty has declined CPR. A sign is taped on the wall near the phone with the 24-hour hospice nurse line in case of emergencies.*
>
> *All family members are encouraged to read the blue pamphlet in the house from hospice entitled "Gone from My Sight," which goes over the stages of dying.*
>
> *Thank you once again for all your prayers, love and support. Keep posting messages, as Patty hears and appreciates all of them.*

I knew we needed to set some limits with visits, so I asked Mom to make a list of people she would most welcome. My hope was that we could save Mom's energy by limiting visits to key people only, rather than tire her with an "open door" policy.

The list ended up being longer than my protective instincts would have preferred. I had to ease up in that regard, as I knew these visits meant a lot to Mom.

Still, my protective feelings emerged more than once. I couldn't reduce the number of visits, so I found myself reducing the length instead. I sometimes wished I had been more eloquent in the way I brought some visits to a close.

It was a tough balance—time with friends and family was important, yet so was conserving Mom's energy and comfort as much as possible.

Vulnerability lies at the center of the family story. It defines our moments of greatest joy, fear, sorrow, shame, disappointment, love, belonging, gratitude, creativity, and everyday wonder.

—BRENÉ BROWN

Leave of Absence

Workplace Support

Earlier that summer, I pulled Dawn aside in the hallway after one of Mom's Mayo appointments. I asked Dawn how I'd know when it was time to take a leave of absence from my job at Eagle's Flight.

All she said was, "You will know."

And she was right.

In August, when Mom prepared to enter hospice, I took an honest look at my workload and talked with my boss and coworkers. I was forthright. I foresaw wanting to be home in Mankato during Mom's final time, yet I referred to her as a "wild card." I didn't know whether she had weeks or months to live.

When hospice began in early September, I made trips back and forth to Mankato while I continued working. But then at 8:00 p.m. on September 10, Dad called Justin and me at home in Minneapolis. Dad said the hospice nurse had suggested he "call the children."

"We're in the car," Justin told Dad. Meaning, we would be there as soon as possible.

And in a few minutes, we were driving the eighty miles to my hometown.

When we got to Mankato, it was late, it was a blur, but it was clear Mom was declining. I knew it was time to be home, to be with her. As heartbreaking as this journey was, I wanted no regrets. I wanted to be able to look back on her final days and know that I made myself available and did everything I could.

The next morning, I called my boss, Dave Root, and asked for time off. It took guts. I didn't know how he'd respond. This was uncharted territory. It's not as if they tell employees at orientation, "If your parent dies or is dying, please take a leave of absence." Still, I took the initiative. I was honest about my needs and asked about my options.

We agreed upon a three-week family leave with an option to extend. I transitioned my workload over to manager Sarah Brandt. I had a lot of projects and duties, so it took some effort. Then Eagle's Flight contracted Sarah Uwimana, a former employee, to cover for me. Gratefully, she agreed.

It was worth it, though, because moving everything over meant I could focus entirely on Mom's needs—and my own. I could step away from my job without worrying one bit.

Knowing my workload would be taken care of filled me with such appreciation for Eagle's Flight. I was humbled by others' willingness to step in for me while still maintaining good customer service and manageable workloads for themselves. I felt fully supported.

Justin was completely supportive of the leave too. He knew it was my place to be with Mom. I would never have this time back.

Dad was extremely thankful to Eagle's Flight as well. He was relieved I would be there to help, especially with things that were out of his element, such as the personal care tasks.

Once my leave began, I went right to Mom's bedside. I told her I wasn't leaving, that I would be there all the time.

"Good," she said.

She knew what was happening.

If you are walking a similar journey with your loved one, I offer you some encouragement: think about what you need to do to live without regrets. Maybe that means taking a leave of absence or at least inquiring about one. Or maybe it means the opposite. Maybe throwing yourself into work is healing and better for you and your family.

Realize you have control over some elements, though not others. Be true to yourself in what works for you, and feel confident in your decisions.

We all have natural abilities and inclinations and find that certain things come easily to us. We may perform a talent so effortlessly that we forget we have it. This is a gift.

—RICHARD J. LEIDER

Taking the Lead
Redefining Roles and Responsibilities

Once we crossed the bridge of hospice, we learned a lot about our family dynamics. Mom had always been the leader of our home and relationships. But there she was, dying. Thus, we had to redefine family roles. We needed a new leader of the home, especially someone who could guide us through the difficult days ahead in the way Mom herself might have.

I first thought Dad would be the leader of our home, but that role was out of his comfort zone. Rather, he had always been the provider for the family.

More importantly, Dad was the last person in the family who wanted to be involved with hospice. We each process things in our own time and own way, and he struggled to wrap his head around it. I first noticed this when he didn't understand that Mom needed to stay home. In retrospect, he didn't grasp the best parts of hospice until after she died.

So in our time of hospice, I found myself taking on the role of leader of the home. Of course, taking the lead isn't the same as doing it all alone. As you'll see in the pages to come, many people played important roles and helped in meaningful ways. In particular, Dad, Justin, Michael, and Julia were active in Mom's hospice journey and shared many responsibilities with me too. To name just a few examples, Michael is an excellent writer, so he wrote a beautiful obituary. Julia is a physical therapist, so she knew how to deal with the medical equipment and was an excellent leader at the hospice intake meeting. We each played on our different strengths.

In my case, though, being the leader of the home meant:

- Taking a temporary leave of absence from work and moving in with my parents
- Being the main point of contact for appointments, visits, and hospice services
- Keeping track of the medication schedule and doses or delegating the task to a specific person
- Helping with medical care—everything from bathing, dressing, and toileting to talking with medical professionals during appointments and visits
- Setting the daily schedule and being the gatekeeper for visitors
- Creating an atmosphere that supported Mom's wish for us to feel comforted and happy

In particular, helping with Mom's personal care was special to me. It felt like a bookend to our physical time together. She cared for me at the beginning of my life; I cared for her at the end of hers.

With this physical connection, I had a strong sense of wanting to stay close to Mom at all times. Going further than the yard made me uncomfortable. I still cherish the nights I slept in a chair beside her hospital bed just so I could hear her breathing and be there if she needed me.

As the new dynamics fell into place, Dad and I got along amazingly well and worked as a team. However, I did have to create a ground rule with him. It was simple. One day, still in my robe at noon, I said, "Dad, I need a shower every day."

From that day onward, I took a shower every morning while Dad sat with Mom to pray and talk together. Mom talked less and less as each day passed. Dad continued to pray out loud even when she couldn't. We sensed she could hear him.

In whatever roles we played, it was such a different time of life. We had to sort out how to cope and operate without Mom running the show.

No one else knows what is appropriate for you—but you do. You always know in the moment what is best for you.

—ESTHER AND JERRY HICKS

The Whole Team
Different Tasks, Different Roles

Being the leader of the home was just one role, and I was just one person. So many other people played so many other important roles. Help came from many sources. We needed it all, and we were deeply grateful.

Mary Ann Brandt continued to coordinate with the "kitchen elves," who regularly delivered meals to the house. My mother-in-law, Sheila Rowland, flew in from Texas. Among other things, she completely managed the kitchen. Mom and Dad's neighbors Al and Sue Kegley graciously welcomed three of our relatives to stay at their home, and Sue made shopping trips for us.

Other loved ones offered spiritual support. Many people prayed the rosary at Mom's bedside. I remember walking by as Nora prayed the rosary while holding Mom's hand. It was an incredibly loving and comforting scene that I still treasure. Mom's friend Pat Matejcek brought Holy Communion to the house and would pray with us. Father John Wilmot came often to pray and bless Mom.

At any given moment, there were a number of people and a variety of things happening in the house, but everyone was respectful of Mom's time to rest. She was in and out of sleep, slowly interacting and conversing less and less.

Sometimes a group would just sit in the room around her, talking and telling stories as she rested. Hearing is one of the last senses to go, so we focused on ensuring she was hearing love and kindness in the home. One time, Sheila was telling a story, and Mom laughed out loud at a funny part when everyone thought she was asleep.

Physical touch was key as well. Often, someone sat bedside, reaching out to touch her arms, head, and legs. Even when she was unable to converse with us, we still felt connected because so many people were there to support her in whatever way we could.

I could go on and on about the roles everyone played and the priceless support they provided. Help was critical and appreciated. The point is, hospice was a time of coming together as a team to support Mom and each other.

I encourage you to consider your family dynamics and the support team you can bring together. When your loved one is in hospice, your circle of family and friends will face many decisions and tasks. Think about how different people can be responsible for different roles.

At the same time, please consider that different people will process the hospice experience in different ways. This is a time of support but also of grief. Rather than judge people on what they're *doing*, offer empathy and understanding about what they're *feeling*.

Every person—of any age—needs space to be honest about their comfort level with different tasks. For instance, someone may prefer running errands rather than being hands-on with medical and personal care. Both roles are equally important.

At all times, give one another permission to be vulnerable and ask for help. You might want to create a distress code word that helps someone express, "I'm in over my head," or, "I'm completely lost." Understand, too, that some loved ones may not participate in the hospice experience at all.

Hospice is a time for coming together as a group as well as honoring our individual needs. Generally, things flow smoothly when we can avoid passing judgments about how others process or the roles they play.

The best gift of a friendship will often be the friend's ability to know what you need even before you do.

—HAROLD KUSHNER

Angel Network
Supporting Me While I Supported My Mom

Mom needed support. So did I.

At age thirty-five, I was the first in my circle of friends to be losing a mother. It was new territory for all of us. My friends Nancy Gnos, Janae Bower, and Holly Locher set up a support team specifically for me. They called it my angel network.

Nancy, Janae, and Holly asked me what type of support I most needed. In an email, I brainstormed several possible ideas—everything from housecleaning and Target runs to prayers and voice mails to "girly" gifts and massage certificates. Because of my limited time and energy, I emphasized that I would appreciate support that didn't need a response or action back from me. For example, I had to be honest about not being able to return dishes or answer phone calls.

Once I put my thoughts together, Nancy, Janae, and Holly spread the word to family and friends. In return, I received a steady stream of support. People sent encouraging cards, prayed for me, provided meals, gifted me spa certificates, and volunteered their time to help with errands. It was wonderful.

I'm grateful for my friends' willingness to give—as well as for my own willingness to receive. I was trying to figure out how to cope with my mother's pending death and how to maintain my sanity at the same time. It would have been so easy to disconnect from my feelings and pretend I could manage it all by myself. Being vulnerable meant being open to loving support. The angels helped my grief process immeasurably.

Whenever I feel that people aren't smiling at me, I simply begin smiling and saying hello, and like magic, there are suddenly more smiling people around me. It is true that your world is only a mirror of you.

—ROBERT T. KIYOSAKI WITH
SHARON L. LECHTER

The Joy Line

Recordings from Loved Ones

As the days passed and Mom continued to surrender, we began making more decisions for her. I was thankful that I had asked her to make that list of important visitors. It was useful to have her input and intentions in advance.

I stayed in communication with the people on Mom's list, keeping them up to date about her status. I was as forthcoming as I could be, given the circumstances. For example, when a close friend from out of town told me she planned to visit Mom in a week, I explained why that would likely be too late, based on Mom's progression. I encouraged the friend to come sooner.

Soon enough, however, we knew we had to limit visitors even more than we had been already. That said, we still knew how important it was for her to hear from loved ones, so we came up with the Joy Line. I shared the idea in my September 12 CaringBridge entry.

> *God is calling Mom to heaven more quickly than we had anticipated. She is staying in the hospital bed in the dining room all the time. The hospice providers have been wonderful and loving to us. Only God will determine the timelines. Due to her energy level, visits are mainly limited to family. We are attempting to create a peaceful, quiet resting place for her and appreciate contact through the CaringBridge guestbook, email, cards, and prayers.*
>
> *The hospice nurse, Leah, said that hearing is the last sense to go.*
>
> *Janae Bower set up an audio recording using the phone and the internet for all of us to use to record a joy message. The purpose of doing this is to surround Patty with joy and laughter during this time. We will be sharing these with Patty. When you call into the number there will be a greeting that will give you the specific information on how to leave a message.*
>
> *We are asking you share with us one or two things: "What brings you joy and laughter in your life?" and the other is, "How has Patty brought joy to your life?" You will have up to five minutes to record your joy message. We appreciate your loving support to share this with us.*

We received many messages on the Joy Line and listened to them as a family in the dining room, where Mom was resting. At that point, she was not interacting with us much. I wonder how much she heard.

The Joy Line had several positive results. For the people leaving the messages, it welcomed them into our experience. It gave them a chance to verbally share one last time during Mom's physical life.

For those of us in the family, the loving words reminded us of Mom's abundant life, even while contrasted with the dying phase. Hearing the voices created a calming presence and sometimes laughter in the room, helping us feel surrounded by love.

There were many beautiful messages. Each was different. In particular, I remember the message from Mom's niece, Laura Rheaume:

> *Occasionally in life you meet people who inspire you . . . who, through their words and actions, remind you of the type of person you want to be. You may only spend moments with them, but they touch you in a profound way, making a lasting change in your life. They become a part of you, a joyful spirit that never leaves you because you so cherish the gift that they brought you: the gift of insight into a better way of life. In this sometimes chaotic world, these visions of the glory of humanity strengthen us and lift us up and help us find our way.*
>
> *Patty, your joy in life, compassion for others, and tireless dedication to friends, family, and positivity have all moved me to embrace those traits in myself. And I smile when I think of you and what you have given me . . . a piece of yourself to treasure all my life. I love you dearly. Grateful to be your niece.*

It is remarkable to deeply love someone and then realize how many other people loved that same person. So many people had a unique connection with Mom. Hearing how Mom impacted others helped ease some of my grief and reminded me of the goodness that keeps growing thanks to her example.

Janae sensed how the Joy Line helped both those giving and receiving the messages. Since then, she's created the Appreciation Line, a special audio product inspired by and dedicated to Mom. This method of collecting messages has been warmly welcomed by others at a variety of milestones in life.

Come to me, all you that are weary and are carrying heavy burdens, and I will give you rest.

—MATTHEW 11:28

Mind-Body-Spirit Connection
Releasing Stress and Processing Grief

I'm a big fan of massage for physical, mental, and emotional well-being. We hold a lot of stress and grief in our bodies. Massage helps loosen the tension and helps our bodies process the feelings.

During hospice, I called Mom's massage therapist and asked if she could come to the house and give Mom a massage in the hospital bed. The massage therapist gladly agreed.

The massage therapist's house call was a kind gift. Mom enjoyed the light massage and the connection. She savored the feeling of relaxation. The massage therapist also gave Michael and me chair massage treatments, which we enjoyed.

Knowing how much Michael and I appreciated the chair massages, I realized that full-body massages would be helpful for those of us so closely involved in the hospice experience. That same week, I called a massage therapist I had been seeing in the Twin Cities. After explaining the situation, I asked if she could bring her massage table and give a few full-body massages in the home. She, too, gladly agreed.

The massage therapist set up her table in an upstairs bedroom, away from the rest of the activities. For the better part of a day, she provided several full-body massages. Dad generously paid the bill, which included a fee per massage, mileage, and a tip.

I know the massages helped us stay healthier, calmer, and more centered. The visible difference on a person's face after a great massage is heartwarming.

Having a massage therapist make a house call is certainly out of the ordinary. But I found that many service providers are willing to do extraordinary things if you reach out and explain your situation. After the experience, my massage therapist wrote and thanked me for my faith and confidence in her to take part in such an intimate time for our family.

When we believe in others and ask for their help, we can discover many special blessings along these journeys. When we honor people's strengths, goodness abounds.

When the heart is flooded with love there is no room in it for fear, for doubt, for hesitation.

—ANNE MORROW LINDBERGH

Yoga

Stretching and Rejuvenating Our Energy

Yoga, like massage, helps the body release the tension it holds within. Suzann Voss, a dear family friend, paid for a yoga instructor to come to the house and lead an hour-long session. It was a lovely gift.

Instructor Mona Ceniceros led Mom's sister Teresa, Michael, and me in a yoga class in the living room. The stretches and positions were calming as well as energizing. Focusing on our breath quieted our minds and eased some of the tension in our bodies.

Throughout the session, we felt a range of emotions. We even laughed over the moans and groans as we all acknowledged how tense and tight our bodies had become. It was fun, healing, and rejuvenating.

My brother and I share a loving family bond, though we process things in our own ways. Doing yoga together, while thinking of our mother lying in a hospital bed in a nearby room, was a form of unspoken connection. It enriched the positive vibe between us and within the home.

The body is a sacred garment. It's your first and your last garment; it is what you enter life in and what you depart life with, and it should be treated with honor.

—MARTHA GRAHAM

When the Time Comes
Preparing to Honor and Bless Her Body

Our friend Laura Turk was visiting. Earlier in Mom's cancer journey, Laura had helped document Mom's life story.

Laura and I sat down in the living room to talk. After a few minutes of conversing, she calmly, tenderly, shifted the conversation.

"Now, Julie . . . have you thought about what you will do when your mother dies?"

All I wanted to do was cry, but I knew I needed to listen. I was focused on what we needed to do during Mom's *dying*. I hadn't given a single thought to what we needed to do upon her *death*.

I knew Laura had experience with at-home death rituals, as one of her best friends had died at home a few years earlier. Laura has a sweet, peaceful, and spiritual demeanor. So I listened, cried, and took notes.

Laura lovingly gave me a vision of what to do shortly after Mom's last breath. She recommended that the first person to know would gently make sure everyone else in the house was aware she

126

had passed and was free from suffering. We were all to gather in the room to experience the immediate moment of her passing.

After this moment together, we were to lovingly disperse the group so the women could ritually prepare the room and Mom's body before welcoming the men and other visitors back in.

Laura emphasized that this ritual would honor Mom, honor those of us grieving, and honor the room itself. After all, it was the dining room of our family home. It wasn't a hospital room we could walk away from when it was over.

She suggested that we especially consider Dad's perspective. This was the home he would continue to live in. It was important to help him avoid uncomfortable memories about the dining room. This ritual would give him the gift of a beautiful goodbye to his wife, a goodbye that would stay with him even after the room converted back to its original purpose.

To this end, Laura helped me understand that the medical supplies didn't need to be part of the picture. For example, she suggested that we turn off the oxygen machine and remove the breathing tubes. Basically, anything medical—the oxygen machine, the medications, sponges, the hospital tray table, and so on—could be removed from the room. We couldn't remove the bed, of course, but we could lower the railings and freshen the sheets. As a finishing touch, we could add a bouquet of flowers, if available.

She suggested that the women then honor and beautify Mom's body. First, we could take off the nightgown, cutting it if we needed to. We could then gently freshen the body with washcloths soaked in warm water and scented bodywash. After drying, we could add scented lotion or perfume.

Next, we could clothe Mom in beautiful new attire as well as drape her body and the bed with scarves or blankets in colors Mom enjoyed. Laura also suggested that we could put a touch of makeup on Mom's face, add a few pieces of jewelry, and gently position Mom's wig in place. Honoring and respecting her was of utmost importance.

While the women were performing this ritual, the men were to carry out an important task as well. Laura recommended that they make calls to notify the "surround list"—the people we wished to gather for a special prayer service. Knowing how difficult it would be to make this call, Laura offered a simple script: "She has passed. You can come by in about an hour." The men could also call the hospice team and the funeral home, instructing them to arrive in about two hours.

When the ritual was complete and all loved ones had gathered, we could join back together in the room. We could share a prayer and a song over Mom as well as share memories and goodbyes if anyone wanted to speak. This would be our time to cry, laugh, breathe, and celebrate. This would be a private time for a few loved ones.

Let me be clear—when Laura gave me these ideas, I felt overwhelmed at first. Worries swirled in my head: *Oh great. Now I need colorful scarves and special lotions . . .? I'm not even leaving the house. How is all this supposed to happen?*

Yet I knew this ritual would be a fitting way to honor Mom. Thanks to Laura, I had a plan and a purpose, and I hoped it would work. In the following pages, you'll learn how collaboration made it all come together.

You, too, may feel overwhelmed as you read this. Very few of us know what to do when a loved one dies at home. Maybe these specific ideas sound odd to you. Once again, trust your instincts about what's right for your loved one and your family and friends. I offer our story just as one example.

My hope is that you give yourself time to prepare for the moments after your loved one's passing. An after-death ritual and ceremony of any kind will honor your loved one and bless you all with grace, dignity, and beauty.

Angel of God, my Guardian dear, to whom God's love commits me here, ever this day be at my side, to light and guard, to rule and guide. Amen.

—GUARDIAN ANGEL PRAYER

Pulling It All Together
Gathering Elements for the Ritual

I was grateful Laura took the initiative to broach the conversation about planning a ritual for Mom's passing. I knew there was a lot to do—and not much time to do it. Thankfully, I had the commitment and support from family and friends to pull the necessary elements together and carry the plan to fruition. It was beautiful how different people contributed in different ways.

I began by collecting things I could find around the house: washcloths, beautiful crystal bowls for water, some makeup, Mom's wig, and more. I arranged all the items on a table in the basement for easy access.

I also selected a dress from Mom's closet to clothe her in for the ritual. It was a long black summer-weight tank dress with a small black-and-white floral-print jacket. I knew that once we put it on Mom for this special ritual, we would not want anyone to wear it later. It would be too emotional to see it on anyone else. Thus, I did not hesitate as I cut the dress and jacket up the back. Then, when the time would come, we wouldn't need to move Mom to dress her. We could lay the clothing on top of her and tuck in the edges.

While I was gathering items around the house, my friend Nancy called and asked what she could do to help. I explained our plan about the ritual and asked her to find lavender body-wash and lotion. Mom was especially fond of lavender, so it seemed fitting. Nancy brought a Thymes lavender gift box with lavender bodywash, lotion, candle, and perfume.

My friend Holly also called and asked what she could do. I explained how I needed large, colorful scarves that would honor Mom's style. I asked her to buy several, and we would return which-ever ones we didn't use. She found some that worked gorgeously.

My mother-in-law, Sheila, added a thoughtful touch—she gave me a colorful shirt with a dahlia flower print. Justin and I grew dahlias in our garden. When the time came, I could wear this special shirt to symbolize the shift in our lives.

In addition to gathering the supplies, I wrote detailed instructions about the women's ritual as well as the men's call-ing tasks. I had the instructions available in the kitchen, and I encouraged loved ones to read them so we would all be aware of plans when the time came. Being specific was helpful. Differ-ent people were present at any given time, so we didn't want to rely only on verbal discussion. Having it all in writing helped us avoid misinterpretation.

The timing was in God's hands, and we were prepared with servants' hearts.

And He will raise you up on eagle's wings
Bear you on the breath of dawn
Make you to shine like the sun
And hold you in the palm of His hand.

—MICHAEL JONCAS, COMPOSER

Tears and Hymns

Expressing Feelings through Music

Mom interacted with us less and less as the disease progressed
in her shrinking body. I called a group of my female friends in
the Twin Cities and asked them to come visit me in Mankato. I
made a special point of inviting my friend Julie Esterley, who is a
remarkable singer. I asked if she would feel comfortable singing
some hymns in Mom's room.

I realized I had given my friends very little notice about this
impromptu gathering. But it must have been meant to be, because
five women were able to make it. I let my family know my friends
were coming. I suggested we have a short prayer service in Mom's
room before Julie would sing some traditional hymns.

When Julie, Kirsten Hargreaves, Pam Kollodge, Mary Towle,
and Annie Madryga arrived, we talked for a couple of minutes
on the porch before heading inside. I used that time to explain
Mom's condition. I painted the picture of what to expect: how

she was hooked up to an oxygen machine, how her eyes were closed, how she wasn't talking or eating much anymore, how it was fine to touch her, and how we were trying to keep the atmosphere peaceful without a lot of noise.

I often explained this to help prepare visitors. It can be difficult to see someone lying in a medical bed in a dining room as they go through the final stages of dying.

Once we headed inside, my friends and family made a circle around Mom's bed. We prayed the Our Father and Hail Mary aloud together. I was closest to Mom. I touched her arm and hand and hugged the upper half of her body at times.

Then Julie sang "Amazing Grace," and I started sobbing. Oprah calls it the "ugly cry." Mine was a soul-wrenching cry of sorrow. It came from deep within and let the pain emerge.

I heard someone comment, "Oh, Julie—don't cry." It's the typical knee-jerk reaction in our culture whenever we see such displays of sadness.

Then someone else said, "Let her cry."

So I cried. Oh, did I cry. After days of leading, welcoming, organizing, listening, coping, and providing care, I felt a huge release physically and emotionally.

I needed it.

That cry has made a lasting impact on me and helped me understand crying and grief. It's interesting—sometimes when you expect tears, they don't come. But other times, unexpected, unplanned emotion comes at you hard from a deep, soulful place, leaving you gasping to breathe normally again.

I broke down because I felt safe with that group of people. I didn't have to be so strong and functional. With those friends and in that moment, I gave myself permission to be vulnerable and to release the pain. I let my guard down, and the pain flooded in and flowed out through the tears.

My friends and family held their positions in the circle during my cry. Some sang. Some cried too. It was a holy experience of release and acceptance. Everyone there held space as they witnessed and shared my tremendous sorrow.

As I allowed the last waves of sorrow to release, a calm came over me. I became more aware of how my friends and family were experiencing this special gathering.

A beautiful thing was how Dad and others joined in with the singing. We usually did not sing in our home, besides the occasional "Happy Birthday to You." Hearing my family sing familiar hymns at home was powerful and deeply resonating.

As we sang, I didn't feel any reaction from Mom. After two or three songs, we asked her if she wanted to hear another song or if she wanted us to stop. It was such an emotional moment, and we didn't want it to be too much for her.

"More," she murmured.

That brought smiles all around the circle. It was gratifying to know she was enjoying it.

Julie led us with "On Eagle's Wings." It was especially sweet to hear Dad singing for the last time to Mom. For years, they had sung these same songs at church, side by side. And now, even though Mom was no longer able to sing, she and Dad could still connect through the beauty of these songs.

Through the years since 2008, my friends have commented how honored they felt to be in Mom's presence during her final days and how the experience impacted their lives. They were—and still are—supportive on my grief journey.

I have never regretted letting them see the depth of my pain that day. I learned what a gift it is to allow someone space to sob and feel safe—and what a gift it is to let go in that moment.

No coward soul is mine.

—EMILY BRONTË

Inspiration and Expression
Writing the Eulogy

I had known since midsummer that I wanted to write a eulogy for Mom. I'd been brainstorming ideas, but I hadn't written anything. But then I woke up in the middle of the night while sleeping in a recliner next to Mom's hospital bed. The eulogy was suddenly pouring into my head.

Everyone else was asleep, but I knew I had to get up and write. I made my way to the kitchen counter, taking the baby monitor with me. I listened to Mom's breathing as I sat and wrote. I believe that God, the angels, and my intention enabled the eulogy to flow from me that night.

Within the next couple of days, I typed up my draft and emailed it to Janae to proofread and enhance. It was helpful to have someone reviewing, editing, and giving input. Among other things, she added a joke to the introduction that echoed all the political campaigning commercials that were on TV at the time.

I love when inspiration guides me. I'm grateful for the download from the heavens in the middle of that night about what to share and how to honor Mom. My love for her is beyond words, so it was a gift to receive words that illuminated even just a glimpse of that love.

Somewhere over the rainbow
Skies are blue
And the dreams that you dare to dream
Really do come true.

—YIP HARBURG, LYRICIST

Therapeutic and Heavenly Music
Inviting a Harpist to the Home

In their gorgeous book, *The Grace of Ordinary Days: An Invitation to Celebrate Life's Journey*, poet Kay Saunders and her son, nature photographer Bernie Saunders, captured connections between a mother and son through life and death. Mom and I both admired the photography and the book.

Bernie lived near Minneapolis, and we had met in person during Mom's cancer journey. While Mom was in hospice, I emailed him and asked if he had any suggestions for how to make the most of this unique time. He recommended Tami Briggs, harpist with Musical Reflections. Bernie wrote, "Tami Briggs, a colleague that I do workshops with, is a therapeutic harpist and plays at people's bedside during these times."

Right away, I liked the idea and contacted Tami. I was excited to give this experience as a gift to Mom. In her reply email, Tami wrote, "It is my greatest honor to play for hospice patients. I am touched that you asked." Luckily, she was available within a week, as I knew Mom wouldn't be with us for many more days.

Tami set up in the dining room, next to the hospital bed. We pulled in additional chairs, as I had invited a few people within Mom's circle of loved ones to join us. I requested that everyone be quiet and not interrupt the music. I wanted Mom to have the full experience of the music touching her soul.

Tami played for an hour. It was peaceful, beautiful, and enriching. While she played, she observed Mom's breathing and paced the music to help Mom continue to release tension.

It was soothing to sit, listen, and just be with others who loved Mom deeply. There was no need to do anything besides enjoy the music that enveloped us.

Emotions would come and go. I held Mom's hand and just kept looking at her as I experienced another layer of saying good-bye. Though her body was rigid, her eyes continually closed, and her jaw clenched, I felt her beauty in my heart.

As she was leaving, Tami commented how she sensed the music's impact on me. She saw a visible change in my body when she played "Somewhere Over the Rainbow." That song resonated in me and released some built-up tension and fear. Her comment helped me realize how the music was therapeutic not only for Mom but for me and the others as well. The experience enriched our lives in countless ways.

I bought CDs of Tami's music and added them to our collection for Mom's ritual. I thought it would be nice to play harp music as we honored her body.

I didn't know it then, but Mom would die the next evening.

Part 5

passing

Grief and pain are opportunities for transcendence—if we're willing to accept them.

—ANGELA WIECHMANN

Leaving Nothing Unsaid

Last Words between Husband and Wife

It was September 17—we knew the end was very near.

Just as Laura Turk gifted me with poignant advice, so she did for Dad. She encouraged him to have a private moment with Mom. I am grateful Laura had such a gentle way of approaching Dad. She recommended he focus on four main areas:

Love: Tell her how much you love her.

Thank you: Express your deep appreciation for her.

Forgiveness: Ask for forgiveness; in any marriage, there is room for forgiveness.

Forgiving: Be forgiving of her, saying, "I forgive you for ___."

So Dad went to Mom's bedside and shared these thoughts with her, even though she was unresponsive.

My parents had many special conversations throughout their marriage. And now Dad will always be grateful for leaving nothing unsaid in their final moments together.

Mom, your soul journey has been strengthened in this lifetime, and the goodness you have revealed will have ripple effects into many lifetimes. I am going to miss you like crazy, but I know we will still be able to connect, and your influence will not end when the body dies. I love you.

—CARINGBRIDGE POST FROM ME

A Million Goodbyes

Letting Go

Dad's special conversation with Mom happened during the final hours of her life. As for me, I don't even remember my last words to her. It might have been something about morphine: "Mom, I'm going to put your medicine in your mouth to help your pain."

At times, I found myself too absorbed in thinking about final words and goodbyes. I wanted them to feel significant and meaningful, with the perfect words at the perfect time.

In retrospect, we had a million goodbyes with Mom.

They started when she received the terminal diagnosis back on Halloween 2005. I'm forever grateful for the time we had between the diagnosis and hospice. It gave us the chance to have many special conversations and meaningful times together. I thank God for that gift. I would have struggled more if Mom had had a sudden death.

Looking back at Mom's cancer journey, I recognize all the subtle goodbyes she said in her own way and in her own time. A pat on a hand. A soft smile. A sigh. She didn't verbalize many of her goodbyes. Maybe that was too difficult because she was living with hope for a longer life.

The goodbyes became more immediate when hospice began, of course. We welcomed Mom's inner circle of family and friends to the home and encouraged them to say goodbye in their own ways. These visits felt sacred, as we knew time was very limited and precious.

In the final hours, those of us closest to her said goodbye by giving her the gift of our acceptance. We wanted her to know it was OK to let go and set herself free of this world. We were ready for her suffering to end.

In our own ways, we each assured her we would be all right. Justin made sure she knew he had Dad set up with a new TV and better reception so Dad could enjoy all the sporting events. Julia and Michael assured Mom that their pregnancy was going well and that the baby would bring new life to the family. I assured her we were planning a beautiful funeral.

Be careful of believing we get to schedule our last conversations with our loved ones. For the record, deathbed scenes in the movies are different than my experience witnessing my mom in real life. She had stopped talking or opening her eyes many hours before her death. So there were no "last words" before her final breath. Time is not ours to know or book. There is no "perfect" moment, but rather only the present moment.

So live your goodbyes every moment, every day. Live a life that expresses your goodbyes in your actions, your values, your beliefs. That way, you will be comforted even if you don't get to express a goodbye with your words.

I have come to believe there are a million goodbyes before every death. Goodbyes in laughter. Goodbyes in simple conversation. Goodbyes in hugs. Goodbye. Goodbye. Goodbye.

I'm grateful I witnessed a million goodbyes with Mom. I experienced them in the present moment, fully felt them, then let them go.

And the goodbyes still continue today.

When we dare to expose the messy, uncurated parts of ourselves to others, it gives them the space to be more vulnerable. To be known deeply—like family—feels really, really good. Sometimes family can be untidy and untamed, but that feeling of belonging is hard to beat.

—JULIE POINTER ADAMS

The Whitehead

The Release

It was evening. The only people in the house were family members. Some were sitting around the kitchen table, talking. Some were surrounding Mom in the dining room. Both rooms were very close, and we all felt connected. My cousin Laura Rheaume had arrived from California within the hour to be with Mom. I was grateful people were gathered.

I was in the dining room. Mom was hooked up to the oxygen machine, which filled the house with a distinct sound. Per the hospice nurse's instructions, we had been administering liquid morphine through her mouth to keep her as pain-free as possible.

Her body looked stiff. She looked so small, as if her weight had vanished into the bed. She had not moved nor communicated anything in any way in many hours. Her eyes were closed.

We didn't know how long she would live. We had read the hospice materials about signs to look for. She had many of them. But it was so hard to tell. I had never been with anyone when they took their last breath.

It was getting late. I started to wonder if Mom would die in the night. I planned to once again spend the night beside her in a chair, yet I still worried that I could perhaps miss the moment if I fell asleep. You don't know the exact timing. Also, Father John Wilmot had informed us that even though we were all staying close to Mom, sometimes a person dies when they sense someone is nearby yet not in the room.

The other family members in the dining room encouraged me to take a bath and get ready for bed. They strongly assured me they were taking care of Mom—and that I needed to take care of myself too.

I was exhausted. I didn't know what to do. I sat a bit longer, then went upstairs to the bathroom. I didn't close the door behind me.

I looked in the mirror. I noticed a whitehead on the side of my nose. I popped it with my thumbnail. I felt a huge release—as if the pressure had been building for hours.

I washed my hands and proceeded to floss my teeth.

Suddenly, Laura came up the stairs and beckoned me. I immediately dropped the floss on a washcloth and raced to the dining room. I saw Julia trying to find Mom's pulse.

Mom was dead.

Family was gathered around the bed. I leaned over the bed and hugged Mom, soul-wrenchingly sad in my heart yet thankful for her not to be in pain anymore.

Later, I found the floss right where I had left it. On the washcloth.

I realized the moment I felt the release from that whitehead was the moment she had taken her last breath.

I was thrilled for her to be in heaven—and, at the same time, completely devastated for us.

Oh, Mom—I miss you.

For every event in life, there are many different angles. When you look at the same event from a wider perspective, your sense of worry and anxiety reduces, and you have greater joy.

—HIS HOLINESS THE DALAI LAMA

The Ritual

Honoring Mom

It was time now. The men began calling. We women began the ritual Laura Turk had helped us prepare.

We removed all medical items (except the bed) from the room. We brought in some flowers and the special items we had stored for this occasion. We played a recording of Tami's harp music.

We put a drape up over the open doorway. We removed the nightgown. Using a large crystal bowl with warm water, we washed Mom's arms, legs, and face with washcloths and the lavender bodywash. We had lush towels to dry her body, then we smoothed the lavender lotion over her body. We could tell how the thin she had become.

It was a time of reverence and saying goodbye. There was a mix of crying, quiet, praying, saying "God rest your soul," and simply being loving. We were in motion, in sync, with focus on the task at hand. It was a holy time.

We draped the dress over her body and tucked in the sides, gently positioned her wig in place, and applied some light powder and blush to her face. Her eyes were closed. Honoring and respecting her was of utmost importance.

We freshened the bed. With the large colorful scarves placed around her and the bed, it no longer looked medical. Instead, it looked lovely and lively.

Once done, we gathered together, both women and men, for prayer around Mom's bed. It was a private moment for a few loved ones. We took time to pray and breathe, time to feel, whether that was shown through crying or laughing.

The mortician arrived shortly after the prayer service and took Mom's body. The next time we would see her body would be at the wake.

The ritual has left a lasting impression on my dad. He frequently tells others that Mom left the home "in style." He can rarely talk about it without his eyes getting glossy because he was so deeply touched.

The ritual also left an impression on Mom's sister Nora. When we first planned it, Nora admitted that she had been unsure about the ritual. With Mom still alive, she was unsure how she'd feel about such an experience after her death. Many times since, though, she has mentioned the beauty and sacredness of the experience, describing it as respectful, loving, and moving.

I see the ritual's lasting impact on the home as well. As Laura had explained, when a loved one dies at home, it leaves some friends and family feeling uncomfortable in the house, especially in the room where the person passed away.

But because of the ritual, we don't feel uncomfortable in the home. Most notably, I haven't seen anyone avoiding the dining room in the years since Mom's death. We have beautiful, special memories of the room from both before and after her death.

Mom was secure and comfortable about taking her last breath at home. The ritual was worthy of that decision—as well as worthy of the life she lived. The ceremony gave us closure and helped bridge the experience between hospice, death, and the ongoing life we all had to live.

Part 6

the services

*Life is fragile. And uncertain. Though
it always has been, we were lulled into
believing we'd eventually get to all the things
on our to-do lists. Yet everyone who's died also
had plans for tomorrow.*

—OPRAH WINFREY

The Announcement
Sharing the News of Mom's Passing

While we female family members performed the special ritual in
the dining room, Dad, Michael, and Justin called many family
and friends. It was heavy news to share.

The CaringBridge website also served as a vehicle to share
the news. Michael posted the message after the mortician came
to take the body. Michael had written it in advance, with input
from the rest of the us.

Dear Friends,

*It is with great sadness that we inform you that Patty
passed away on Wednesday, concluding her courageous bat-
tle with lung cancer. If you are able to make the trip to
Mankato, our family would be honored to have you participate in a celebration of Patty's life. Patty spent a considerable*

*amount of time planning her funeral arrangements, and
we want to share those plans with you.*

Because we had been able to finalize plans with the funeral
home and church that same night, the CaringBridge post went
on to include detailed information about the upcoming wake
and the funeral. Being so thorough on CaringBridge helped us
immensely. We could avoid lots of follow-up questions because
we were transparent and complete in our communications.

The consolidated contact list, which Mom and I had worked
on, was helpful during this time of grief. It allowed us to spread
the news efficiently. The database included details about Mom's
various social circles, such as her high school friends and college
friends. We could call one person from each social circle and then
ask them to inform the others.

In a similar way, my coworker John Reid helped spread the
word at Eagle's Flight. John and I had worked closely throughout
Mom's cancer journey. When I was preparing for my leave of
absence, I asked if he would be willing to leave a voice mail for
the entire company once Mom died. I wanted everyone to know
and hear the same way. John did a beautiful job with the message,
emphasizing how Mom's spirit would live in me.

As heavy as our hearts felt, we did our best to spread the
word to the key contact people in Mom's life and our own individual lives. That way, we knew the wake and funeral would be
wonderful celebrations and tributes to her life. We could gather
to cry, laugh, and comfort one another.

*It's okay, honey, you can let it all out...I
know you've been hurt, and I know you're
angry and confused. So, go ahead and let it
out. It does a soul good to let the waters run
once in a while—the healing waters.*

—WM. PAUL YOUNG

Reiki

Improving the Flow of Life Energy

Mom's death impacted me emotionally, physically, and spiritually. Laura Turk recommended a local Reiki practitioner, so I scheduled a session for the morning before the wake.

The word *reiki* (pronounced *ray-key*) means "universal life energy" in Japanese. Through energy healing, visualization, and other simple techniques, Reiki practitioners detect and alleviate energy flow problems on the physical, emotional, and spiritual levels. Like traditional massage therapy, Reiki can relieve stress and pain as well as improve the symptoms of various health conditions.

I may have had the loudest reaction ever to Reiki that morning. Wails of sadness and deep grief emerged from me through most of the treatment. The cries were from deep in my chest. I could hardly catch my breath at times. The treatment was not physically painful. Rather, my cries reflected the grieving energy releasing from my body.

How often are we afforded the time and space to cry our whole heart out and not have to worry about anyone else feeling uncomfortable or responsible for comforting us or calming us down? During the session, I let it all out, and no one took it personally, was upset by my actions, or needed an explanation.

It was a bit like the moment when I cried while my friends sang at Mom's bedside. Only this was much more intense physically.

Grief needs to be released in order for healing to begin. The release can happen many ways—anything from crying, talking, singing, and thinking to exercising, cuddling, and resting. For me, Reiki allowed that physical release and healing. I had received Reiki treatments before, but that session was unlike any other I had—or have since—experienced.

We hear countless stories about people who go to excess when it comes to eating, spending, sex, using drugs and alcohol, and on and on. When people go to extremes, many times it's because unprocessed grief is driving their behavior.

Thankfully, my friends and family have shown and modeled ways to release and live through my grief. These healthy, productive behaviors have enhanced my life.

That Reiki session did more than release the energy of my grief. It also allowed me to experience a deep spiritual connection to Mom and Grandma Keenan. In the midst of my wails, I heard them sending me messages.

Messages of hope.

They said they loved me, that everything was going according to plan, and that my experiences with death and grief would be of great service to God in the future. They told me I was a channel—I was to use their stories of hospice and death to enrich and teach others about the final phases of life.

As they spoke, I kept agreeing, often verbally. "I know. OK, I know," I'd say.

The messages were inspiring as well as overwhelming. As wondrous as it was, I would have traded it to have them healthy, happy, and alive.

The timing of that Reiki session was a monumental gift. It was a life-affirming experience on one of the hardest days of my life.

I understood that every flower created by Him is beautiful, that the brilliance of the rose and the whiteness of the lily do not lessen the perfume of the violet or the sweet simplicity of the daisy. I understood that if all the lowly flowers wished to be roses, nature would lose its springtime beauty, and the fields would no longer be enamelled with lovely hues. And so it is in the world of souls, Our Lord's living garden.

—SAINT THÉRÈSE OF LISIEUX

Bouquets of Love

Floral Arrangements

Mom had told us there would be many floral arrangements at her wake and funeral. She didn't state it in a boastful way but in a matter-of-fact, it's-just-what-happens-at-funerals type of way. She had seen how many arrangements people sent for Grandma Keenan's funeral in June 2001.

Plus, Mom knew there would be a lot of floral arrangements because her deep love and appreciation for flowers and plants were no secret. Everyone knew she loved her garden and loved talking about flowers and plants. Her art, her home decor, and even some of her attire featured flowers. Sending a floral arrangement would be a fitting and loving gesture to pay respects and honor Mom's life.

As it turned out, Mom was right. People sent flowers. *A lot* of flowers.

Our immediate family had private time to see the casket, flowers, and gifts before guests arrived for the wake. When we walked into the funeral home, we were amazed and in awe. So many gorgeous and creative bouquets and plants. We walked from arrangement to arrangement, reading each floral card.

We were so touched and honored at this living, blooming outpouring of love.

O Divine Master, grant that I may not so much seek to be consoled as to console; to be understood as to understand; to be loved as to love.

—PEACE PRAYER OF SAINT FRANCIS OF ASSISI

The Wake

An Evening of Celebration and Sympathy

We held the wake the evening before the funeral. It was a time for visitation and prayer. I was thankful that we had a chance to get settled before the other guests arrived.

The funeral home did a nice job of preparing Mom. Her blue dress was vibrant and beautiful.

They also made a handout with her photo. I was grateful we were able to supply them with a somewhat current professional photo—taken when she still had her own hair. The photos from that session have become lasting keepsakes of Mom looking beautiful, vibrant, and healthy.

We also displayed some wonderful photo boards Julia created in the short time between Mom's death and the wake. Mom loved photos, so it was fitting to have some on display at her wake.

In retrospect, I wonder why we as a family didn't prepare the photo boards earlier. Did we think it would be too hard? Maybe we would have enjoyed going through photo albums together as a family, collecting favorite snapshots. Or maybe it would have been too painful to face the reality that these photos would be displayed only once Mom was gone.

After our private family time, guests soon began arriving. Many people came. The attendance was humbling. We could see and feel the love surrounding us. It was comforting.

However, some aspects of the evening were challenging. Unfortunately, most people are uncomfortable with death and grief, which can lead to awkward conversations and interactions.

Lots of people felt compelled to tell me about the loved ones they themselves had lost. Even if it was well meaning, I didn't find it helpful. A wake is a time to honor the person who passed and to comfort and support the family. It's not a time for guests to focus on themselves and their experiences. I found myself comforting others, which I really didn't want to be doing at my mom's wake.

Other people really didn't know what to say or how to say it, so they defaulted to small talk. I wasn't in the mood to answer such things as, "So, where do you work?" Frankly, my career was not on my mind—not with my mom in that box over there.

Thankfully, some special people did understand this was a time to honor Mom and our family's grief. Someone saying a simple "I love you" was enough to touch my heart. For some, they didn't have to say anything at all; the fact that they showed up was a comfort.

Some cherished loved ones asked me how I was doing with all the emotion of the evening. I remember telling them that the wake was much easier than the sad, grueling days leading up to it. Although I did get emotional at times throughout the evening, the deep cries in the private Reiki session earlier in the day helped me show up as best as possible. Some of my closest friends could see the impact the energetic healing had had on me.

Of course, the wake was a different experience for each of us family members. In particular, I remember Grandpa Keenan saying to people, "Shouldn't outlive your child."

We all grieve differently, even for the same person. We all have our own timelines and reactions. We need to respect what people can do and how they can show up.

That night, after the wake, turned out to be special too—thanks to a simple, unexpected act of love and support.

I was sitting at the kitchen counter, firming up the eulogy with help from my WINGS sisters, Janae and Sara. Dad was watching a ball game in the living room. Then, all of a sudden, two of my other closest friends, Nancy and Holly, came in with a greasy hometown Pagliai's Pizza.

Nancy said later that the late-night pizza was her favorite moment out of all the events that week. She could tell how much it meant to Dad to not be alone and to do something as *normal* as enjoy a pizza. It was a nice way to cap off a long day.

And the funeral was the next morning.

The Archbishop expressed it quite wonderfully when he explained, "We don't really get close to others if our relationship is made up of unending hunky-dory-ness. It is the hard times, the painful times, the sadness and the grief that knit us more closely together." A funeral is perhaps the most obvious example of this weaving of our relationships and community together, but even tears are a signal to others that we need comfort and kindness, that we are vulnerable and need help.

—HIS HOLINESS THE DALAI LAMA AND
ARCHBISHOP DESMOND TUTU
WITH DOUGLAS ABRAMS

Honoring Last Wishes

Some Thoughts on Memorial Services

I believe in the value of some type of gathering after someone dies—a funeral, a memorial, a celebration of life. Something to bring people together to honor and celebrate the life as well as mourn the loss. In Mom's case, we had a Catholic Mass of Resurrection at my parents' church.

161

What type of gathering you have depends on your desires, faith, and family and cultural traditions. And as we've discussed earlier in the book, it's ideal if you know how your loved one wants their life to be celebrated and honored.

Mom was very clear, for example, about her wishes—down to the hymn selections. She was often more eager to discuss her funeral plans than I was, but I'm so grateful we worked through it together.

In contrast, some people wish to not have a funeral or gathering upon their death. Justin's parents, Tom and Sheila Rowland, expressed such a desire, and we respected their wishes upon their deaths. Even though I personally value funerals, I place greater value on respecting people's wishes. Thus, I did not feel guilty or regretful when Tom's and Sheila's deaths passed without official ceremonies.

Each person is unique, and so are their wishes. Whenever possible, knowing those wishes prior to a loved one's passing makes implementing things more peaceful for all. It's never too early to talk about this with your loved ones—or to talk about it yourself.

I hope I go to heaven. If I do, I'll put in a good word for all of you.

—MY MOM, PATTY JOHNSON

The Funeral

A Tribute to a Well-Lived Life

Then it was time—the funeral. Nearly three years had passed since that Halloween night when Mom shared the news of her diagnosis. And now here we were. This was the moment we had always known would arrive too soon.

As people entered the church, they received the funeral program Janae and I created with input from the family. We had worked on it while Mom was still in hospice.

We also created a special bookmark to hand out after the service as a commemorative item. The bookmark was an appropriate way to honor of Mom's life—she loved reading and teaching. The bookmark showcased my friend Sara Weingartner's beautiful dragonfly artwork (more about dragonflies later), and we included the heaven quote from Mom that's featured at the beginning of this vignette. It showed both her humility and humor.

The program and bookmark turned out so well. They reflected not only who Mom was but the quality of life she had led. They added a special touch to the service, similar to how she had touched many lives.

163

The church quickly began to fill with people. Many attended, just like at the wake. It felt comforting to those of us deeply grieving.

Many friends and family had roles and responsibilities within the service, such as greeting, singing, reading, pallbearing, passing out the bookmarks, and more. It added to the uniqueness of the celebration.

Not everyone felt comfortable taking on a special role, however. For some, just facing the grief and the weight of the day was enough. They didn't feel emotionally or physically capable of assisting with the service. In these cases, honesty and respect was best for all.

Michael and I both delivered eulogies during the beginning portion of the service. You can read them in the pages to come.

I spent the morning finding the courage and strength to deliver the eulogy. It helped that Holly took me to Aveda to have my hair styled (I wanted to have a good hair day) and then listened as I read through the eulogy on the way to the church. We both loved it and knew I could do it.

That said, I did ask Janae if she would read the eulogy as my backup plan, in case I was too emotional to speak. And I did need to keep repeating positive words over and over to myself. I reminded myself that if I started to cry, I could read the tips I had typed to myself right on my script:

Look up and to the left—it closes the tear ducts. (I knew exactly where this spot was in the balcony. As it turned out, my college friend Sarah Way happened to be sitting there. That was an unexpected comfort to me.)

Stop. Breathe. Compose. Continue.

Relax shoulders.

I volunteered to give my eulogy first. I was concerned about not being able to literally stand and deliver if I waited too long before speaking. I was so weak and exhausted with grief that I could hardly walk or stand. I also wanted to go first because I didn't know how emotional I would get listening to Michael's eulogy.

Eventually, it was time for my eulogy. I rose from the pew I shared with Dad and made my way up to the pulpit. Nancy told me she knew I would do fine just by the way I walked.

I needed to hold the pulpit tightly, yet somehow the strength came. I was able to deliver words I felt were worthy of my mother. I am grateful I rose to the occasion. Being able to give that eulogy the way I did—it was a culmination of everything in my life. It was a highlight of my life and one of the greatest gifts I ever gave her.

After my eulogy, it was Michael's turn. The first thing he did when he got to the microphone was make a joke about how we as siblings are very different and so are our eulogies. People laughed—Dad and I especially. With that, Michael was off to a great start for this milestone moment in his life, when he would share about the mother he had lost.

And it was true—our eulogies were different. Our words did not overlap too much for the listeners. It helped that I had read his eulogy prior to the service to be sure that between the two of us, we had covered all the details we wanted communicated from the family.

For months afterward, Dad received compliments around town about how special the eulogies were. Each of us was able to express our love and fond memories about Mom in our own way.

After the service, many of us went to the cemetery for the burial, then we enjoyed a lunch back at the church gym with the attendees. Julia had organized the food order. It was a catered meal, and I remember people enjoyed it.

As the large gathering time came to an end, I took comfort. It was a fitting tribute to a life well lived.

My goal is not to remain the same but to live in such a way that each day, year, moment, relationship, conversation, and crisis is the material I use to become a truer, more beautiful version of myself. The goal is to surrender, constantly, who I just was in order to become who this next moment calls me to be.

—GLENNON DOYLE

Eulogy by Julie

Inspiration and Expression

The following is the eulogy I delivered at Mom's funeral.

I am Julie Wylie, lucky and proud daughter of Doug and Patty Johnson—and I approve this message. [*The crowd laughed.*]

Thanks for the laugh. Good one, Janae!

So, I've asked a few people recently for advice on how to give a eulogy, and some said, "It isn't the time to canonize the person—don't make the person a saint." You need to talk about some of their foibles and make them sound human. And when I thought about the people who gave me the advice not to canonize her, I realized they didn't know my mom.

Therefore, instead of foibles, I've decided to tell you three things about Mom in relation to God, teaching, and joy.

1. God

I work on dissolving barriers to God in my life. Mom, she always had a direct, clear channel to God. Whether it was doing the dishes and saying, "Jesus, Mary, Joseph," or during a hailstorm saying the Our Father prayer while she pulled the ugly big black chair over Michael and me as the windows broke . . . she kept the connection to God alive.

She truly believed in and embraced God—calling out to God through prayer for help, love, and support for herself as well as for all of us.

Mom dedicated her life to serving God in many ways—through the church, through the religious organizations, and through using her God-given gift of teaching.

2. Teaching

These days, it's so popular to find your life's calling and know your purpose. After Mom realized dating was fun and maybe she wouldn't be a nun—which was real lucky for Michael and me, since we became her children [*the crowd laughed here too*]—she followed her life's purpose of teaching.

She was a teacher to the *core*—whether it was teaching in schools or getting everyone's attention at the Keenan brunch on Christmas over a framed photo of an eagle. While I was sitting with her the other night, I put a photo on the website of her with the eagle picture. She bought it from a guy at a craft fair in the mall. She could tell us all about the eagle *and* all about the guy's craft fair business, and she really had our attention. She'd tell us both stories, and somehow we'd all be listening and laughing, brought about by her zest for learning and passing it on.

Mom courageously accepted the cancer journey.

The day after the diagnosis, she made a conscious decision to "be living with cancer," and by the grace of God, she focused on hope. Through that conscious decision to be living with cancer, focused on hope, she was able to publicly share her entire cancer journey over CaringBridge.org.

We were sitting at Mayo, waiting for an appointment. It's really nice at Mayo on the oncology floor—they have internet and everything. So, I said to Mom, "You want one of those websites?" She said, "*Ohhhhh*, yes!" [*The crowd laughed.*] Can't you just hear her?! "Oh, yes—people can learn from my story. I don't want others to go through what I am going through with lung cancer." So, the website became another classroom, and in return, we "students" tuned in, learned, and listened.

The word *inspiration*—which means "in spirit"—started popping up in the website guestbook entries. She said to me, "People are saying *I'm* an inspiration." And she was surprised. She was surprised because she was just being herself, not trying to be an inspiration, but rather just living her life's calling of teaching and learning.

While we are all grateful for the special things Mom taught each of us, holding them dearly in our hearts, we are especially thankful for her teaching us about joy.

3. Joy

The movie *The Bucket List* (or as my friends tell me—I haven't been able to watch it yet) is about two men crossing off all the things they want to do in life before they "kick the bucket." *Joy* comes up as the secret to life—in the ability to *find joy* yourself and *give joy* to others.

The Lord also teaches us to find and give joy in this verse: "Do not grieve, for the joy of the Lord is your strength."

Mom was wired for joy. She wasn't a big crier (even when I really wanted her to cry) and was always finding the silver lining. She could find *big, expressive joy* over a good piece of chocolate or a pretty wall color in someone else's home. If there was joy to be found, she found it.

In August, when we were at the lake home and she had decided to go into hospice, we talked about what she wanted to focus on. For Mom, the two main themes that emerged were *joy* and *laughter*.

When she was diagnosed with cancer, she made the decision to live with cancer and have hope. As she transitioned into hospice, she consciously focused on joy and laughter, which resulted in one of the greatest lessons she ever taught and modeled: BE JOYFUL!

So, where did her connection to God, love of teaching, and her focus on joy get her?

I believe to heaven, with this fond farewell from earth surrounded by all your love—and support and joyful blessings.

Here is what my mom said a few weeks ago; some of us here were sitting around her when she said it: "I hope I go to heaven." [*The crowd laughed.*] I know! I said to her, "If you're *not* going to heaven, I don't know who is." But she said, "I hope I go to heaven. If I do, I'll put in a good word for all of you."

Thanks, Mom—we're counting on you!

There's Michael—isn't he handsome?!

—A COMMENT MOM, IN ALL SERIOUSNESS,
OFTEN OOZED ABOUT MICHAEL

Eulogy by Michael

Honoring Her and All Involved

The following is the eulogy my brother, Michael, delivered at Mom's funeral.

Thank you all for coming today. My mother was the consummate hostess, and no one ever left her home hungry. She certainly would not want anyone to leave her funeral hungry, so we are going to have a Minnesota little lunch after the burial. We would be honored if you could join us.

Our family wishes to especially thank Father Wilmot for all your support. Father Wilmot visited or called nearly every day during my mother's illness, and your visits helped my mother find peace. My mother's Catholic faith was central to her identity, and she was blessed to have Father Wilmot at her side during these difficult years.

We also wish to thank all of the medical providers who cared for my mother. The doctors, nurses, and everyone who cared for my mother were incredible. We cannot thank you enough for the care you provided. The medical professionals did everything possible to treat the cancer and to care for my mother's emotional needs.

Our family thanks all of you for coming today. My mother believed that the saints and angels walked among us. They were not just sculptures or pictures; they were living souls. During her illness, my mother was visited by many saints and angels. When someone sent her a card or took the time to write a comment on her CaringBridge site, you were my mother's angel. When someone brought her a meal or visited her, she thought of you as a saint. And when a person went golfing with my father and got him out of the house for a couple of hours, you were an archangel. [*The crowd laughed.*]

During my mother's illness, I had several conversations with people as to whether it is better to die suddenly and unexpectedly or to have a long, difficult death like my mother. There is no good answer to that question. However, because of the way my mother died, I was able to learn so much about her that I otherwise would not have known.

During her illness, I learned just how tough my mother was. She went through four series of chemo, which included up to six sessions per series. Often, she went home and cleaned the house after receiving the chemo. She also had radiation on her brain and lost her hair three times. Through it all, she did not complain about her suffering, even though some complaining would have been justified. She was so tough that she was still helping to split wood just a few months ago. Her willingness to split wood during her illness was not only a testament to her toughness but also to her dedication to my father.

Over these past several years, I also learned how many people my mother impacted. My mother believed that everyone in her life was there for a reason, and she had a gift for making friends quickly. She could make a friend during an elevator ride and knew the life stories of many grocery store workers. Numerous people who met her once made postings on her CaringBridge website. My mother also treated everyone she met equally. Whether she was visited by a friend or the bishop, she treated each person equally as a child of God.

The large number of people who attended the wake last night and are here today is a great testament to my mother's impact on others.

Thank you, all, for being angels to my family during these trying times. I wish I could be like Lou Gehrig and tell you not to worry about us, but we could use your continued prayers over the coming months. Thank you.

*May the stars carry your sadness away, may
the flowers fill your heart with beauty, may
hope forever wipe away your tears.*

—CHIEF DAN GEORGE

Blooming Gifts

Giving Away the Floral Arrangements

When we pulled into Dad's garage right after the funeral lunch, we were welcomed by all the floral arrangements. The funeral home had delivered them after the service. It was a beautiful sight—but also a little overwhelming.

There were too many to keep. Watering and keeping them all fresh would have been quite time-consuming.

Plus, I simply didn't want to keep them all. I came to realize that each arrangement would eventually die, and it would make me feel a new wave of sadness. They would be more examples of death. In contrast, giving away arrangements while they were still gorgeous would feel very gratifying and healing.

Thankfully, Mom had prepared me so well. She had made a one-page handwritten list of people and places who could receive the extra arrangements—everything from dear neighbors and friends to the church and a nursing home.

As other family members rested, I went to her file, pulled out the list, and got to work. I started selecting which arrangements to keep and which to give away. Through it all, Mom's list was extremely helpful. Her foresight was an incredible, generous gift—one I appreciated while riding a roller coaster of emotions after the funeral.

I called Sara Geiman and Michelle Voss to help make the deliveries. Sara and Michelle are sisters and my lifelong friends. With their help, it all flowed so well. We enjoyed spreading the beauty about town.

Based on comments from those who received plants and bouquets, I knew the arrangements helped their grieving process and made things a little lighter and more beautiful.

Let us build the city of God. May our tears be turned into dancing. For the Lord, our light and our love, has turned the night into day.

—DAN SCHUTTE

Family Dinner
Private Celebration and Tradition

There was one last gathering—the private family dinner at the golf club. This event included our intimate family, my parents' siblings and their spouses, and my adult cousins plus their spouses and children. People came together from multiple states, and many age groups were represented.

Although we all had attended the wake and funeral, we never had the time or space to truly come together as a family. There were so many other people and so many tasks. The golf club event allowed us to gather solely as a family. At last, we could talk, laugh, and grieve together.

During the dinner, I gathered the sisters, sisters-in-law, and goddaughters and gave them the jewelry pieces Mom had picked out for them, with my help. All the pieces were in gift boxes or bags, and I asked that they be opened later, in private. Mom had put great thought into matching each piece to each recipient. I didn't want it to become a comparison show.

After the meal, we had an open-microphone time. Many people shared favorite memories of Mom or favorite quotes from her. Others shared how they were feeling. Some told jokes. It was healing to laugh and cry together.

I am grateful Mom had the great foresight to plan this event. It was a time of healing and coming together—exactly as she had wanted it.

These dinner celebrations have become a tradition for us now. It began with Grandma Keenan's funeral, then Mom added to the tradition, and since then, we've had a dinner for Grandpa Keenan.

I hope this tradition continues.

Part 7

life without

her alive

*Of the many relationships we have in life,
few make as profound an impact as the one
we share with our mother. That connection,
whether strong or strained, influences who
we become in countless ways. It teaches us
how to be—or how not to be—adults, partners,
and parents to our own children.*

—OPRAH WINFREY

Reprogramming
Even the Little Things Change

In the first weeks and months after Mom died, my brain needed reprogramming. It wasn't an easy process. Grief unexpectedly hit me countless times, even over the seemingly smallest details.

I had to get used to talking in the past tense about Mom. Instead of saying "she is," I needed to switch to "she was." It was mentally jarring and emotionally unsettling.

I struggled to figure out what to call the home Mom had lived in my entire life. Growing up, it was "our home." Once I was an adult, it was "my mom and dad's home." For many months after she died, I called it "my parents' home." Later, I came to call it "my dad's home."

I kept forgetting to set the table for five, not six, when the family was together. For months after, I had to catch myself as I counted the number of plates or forks. Not physically including Mom at a meal was so foreign to me.

Since then, I have learned that some cultures add an extra place setting in honor of their ancestors. The small gesture helps the family remember their loved ones in present-day activities.

From my own experience, I can understand why some people adopt that tradition. I'm not sure, though, whether the tradition would have been comforting to me or whether it would have added to my grief.

Of all the little ways I had to reprogram, learning that I couldn't telephone Mom was—and still is—the toughest. I still think about calling her, and then I have to remind myself I can't anymore. I've considered talking out loud in my car and pretending I was on the phone with her, but I haven't figured out how to make that feel natural or fun.

So many changes—little and big.

We ought always to thank God for you,
brothers and sisters, and rightly so, because
your faith is growing more and more,
and the love all of you have for one another
is increasing.

—2 THESSALONIANS 1:3

Leave of Absence

Workplace Support

I knew I needed time to handle post-funeral tasks such as thank-you notes and giving Mom's things away. More importantly, I knew I needed to be with friends and family—especially Dad and Justin. It was a vulnerable time in my life.

So I extended my leave of absence from Eagle's Flight for a total of six weeks. The leave gave me the time to focus on my family and my grief.

I will always be grateful for the people who made my leave possible and who encouraged me to focus on my family full time. Most of my coworkers were spread throughout the US and Canada. They supported me so much during my journey through conversations, cards, emails, and guestbook entries on the CaringBridge site. I was able to see some of my Minnesota coworkers at the wake and funeral.

In response to this support, I woke up early on September 23—six days after Mom died. I suddenly felt compelled to leave a voice mail to the company. To bolster my courage and make it through without crying, I wrote out my message so I could read it:

Hey, Eagle's Flight—it's Julie Wylie. Thanks for the great outpouring of support and love surrounding my mom's passing. I can feel the prayers. Thanks for the donation to CaringBridge in memory of Mom. Thanks for the leave of absence and flexibility in shifting the work.

From the bottom of my heart, thanks for the everyday type of support and encouragement you've given me since May 2000, when I met many of you at an Enigma session in West Virginia at the Greenbrier. You have helped me develop into a woman capable of giving a eulogy to a balcony-packed funeral for a mother I ache for.

One of the things I focused on in the eulogy was joy and Mom's ability to find and give it. We created joy bookmarks in celebration of Mom, and I'll bring some to the office to distribute so each of you can have one.

Thank you. God bless.

I know the voice mail had impact in ways I never imagined. My coworker Connie Barber made note of it in a sympathy card: "Thank you for the voice mail. I was concerned for you and your family, so it was wonderful to hear your voice."

After some time passed, I gathered with some coworkers for a nice lunch at a restaurant. These little acts of staying connected would ease the way for my return to work down the road.

I'm thankful I found the courage to ask for family leave time, for Eagle's Flight's generous response, and for the difference it made to our family. As before, I encourage you to ask your company for family leave—you might be surprised how generous and supportive they are.

I always hear that old adage that no one on their deathbed wishes they'd spent more time at the office. We should especially keep this in mind during moments of bereavement, family crisis, or other emotionally charged experiences. There isn't a lot of time or space for grief in the workplace. Taking time off helps us be our best selves.

In retrospect, I know my leave of absence made me a stronger contributor once I returned to work. After six weeks, I felt ready to focus and function as normal so I could fulfill the tasks within my role.

What we have once enjoyed we can never lose.... All that we love deeply becomes a part of us.

—HELEN KELLER

Sympathy Cards
Sentiments of Grief and Love

Mom sent hundreds of sympathy cards during her life. It was just one of the ways she showed love and support. In turn, we received an abundance of cards at the wake and funeral and in the mail after her death.

Dad and I dedicated time to opening the cards. We read and absorbed each one. There was a range of emotions in the process.

It was humbling to read the sentiments. It was yet another way to recognize our grief. We graciously accepted the comforting words. Dad and I often commented on how touching the communications were and how thankful we were to receive them. Mom had touched so many lives.

We kept all the cards out so others in the family could read them too. And we made sure to keep each card with its envelope, making it easier for addressing the thank-you notes.

Janae Bower and Sara Weingartner created thank-you cards that matched the design of the funeral program, and my uncle

Joe Keenan helped get them printed. Inside each card was the following message of gratitude:

> *We are feeling the loss of Patty so deeply yet are comforted by everyone's sympathy and generosity. As you know, Patty was a wonderful woman who loved her family, friends, and community with all her heart. We are humbled and touched by your thoughtfulness.*
> *Gratefully,*
> *The Doug Johnson Family*

After we sent thank-you notes, I selected my favorite sympathy cards and arranged them into pretty scrapbooks. In retrospect, the whole process—receiving and reading the cards, thanking people, and putting my favorites into scrapbooks—was healing on my grief journey.

The truth is that we don't know if we are
going to die tomorrow. Who knows? We have
the idea that we have many years in the
future. But do we?

—DON MIGUEL RUIZ

Generosity and Sympathy
Memorials and Donations in Mom's Name

As part of the outpouring of sympathy, many people made donations as memorials to Mom. Her generous heart had touched many lives; it was humbling to see the generosity people expressed in return.

Thanks to Mom's initiative, we already knew which organizations she had designated for the memorials. Michael was able to include the list right in her obituary:

> *In honor of Patty's life and her commitment to service, memorials may be made to: The Patricia and Douglas Johnson Endowment for Religious Education at Loyola Catholic School, Schola Foundation, St. Joseph the Worker Catholic Church, Pathstone Living (FKA Mankato Lutheran Home), or Birthright.*

In addition to those listed in the obituary, other organizations—such as Rotary, CaringBridge, Mankato Hospice, and the American

Cancer Society—were also recognized through memorial donations. The organizations receiving the donations were appreciative.

In particular, we were overwhelmed by people's generosity toward the endowment fund. People knew Mom and Dad's love of spirituality and education, and they trusted that the endowment would serve the greater good.

The endowment would be funding youth and staff retreats through Youth Frontiers, an organization founded by Joe Cavanaugh. In August, Mom and Dad decided that Youth Frontiers would be a formidable way to utilize the endowment—only, we didn't have enough funds at the time.

Three weeks later, Mom died, the memorials started pouring in, and the endowment grew. What began as the seed of an idea between Mom and Mary Ann Brandt was now bearing fruit.

Whether they were to the endowment or to other organizations, the generous donations in Mom's memory were incredibly touching. It was an honor to see how her legacy helped support so many important missions.

What do people fear most about death?
I asked the Reb. "Fear?" He thought for
a moment. "Well, for one thing, what
happens next? Where do we go? Is it what
we imagined?" That's big. "Yes. But there
is something else." What else? He leaned
forward. "Being forgotten," he whispered.

—MITCH ALBOM

Lake Property Legacy

Support from Life Insurance Funds

My parents were always clear about their intentions for the lake home. They knew they wanted it to stay in the family even after they were gone. For tax and inheritance purposes, they set up a legal partnership agreement detailing how the ownership would pass through generations. I've always found it comforting to understand their vision and desires.

As Mom's deteriorating health became more evident, she knew the lake home would continue to be a place of family gatherings in the weeks—and years—after her death. She also realized, however, that her children and their spouses would be focused on paying for the upkeep of their own homes. We would need extra funds to maintain and improve the lake home as well.

It was easy, then, to understand why Mom chose to leave a large portion of her life insurance death benefit to the lake home partnership. Now, we can use the insurance money to pay for the upkeep and improvements, deciding as a family which project is most urgent.

It's a blessing and an example of Mom's legacy.

*When we honestly confront the things we
own, they evoke many emotions within us. . . .
Believe what your heart tells you when you
ask, "Does this spark joy?" If you act on that
intuition, you will be amazed at how things
will begin to connect in your life and at the
dramatic changes that follow. It is as if your
life has been touched by magic.*

—MARIE KONDO

Beginning the Process
Sorting and Donating Mom's Belongings

Soon after the services, most family and friends went back into
their usual schedules. Thanks to my leave of absence at work, I
could go back and forth between Mankato and Minneapolis and
devote as much time as possible to sorting through Mom's things.

Dad and I agreed that the contents of a home are meant to
serve the *living*. The task, then, was to go through all of Mom's
belongings. Some things we planned to donate or gift, as we
knew Mom's wish for things to be used. Other items would be
simply tossed out. Mom wouldn't have wanted us to get all sentimental about such things as her toothbrush or last razor. We
set up a system of boxes and bags marked "Donate" and "Trash."

In those first few days, I quickly realized just how much could be stored in a single closet or drawer. The work was time consuming.

As it turned out, the process would take years—long after I returned to work and resumed my usual routine. I did as much as I could during my leave of absence, then I eventually blocked out a weekend a month. As much as possible, I trusted the timing of things.

The project felt more manageable when I focused on one area at a time. For example, it helped to stick to just one closet and not sidetrack myself with the photos in the living room at the same time. Completing one area at a time kept the house in order, kept the daily number of decisions to a realistic amount, and gave us a sense of completion at the end of each day.

With Mom's clothes alone, we faced many decisions: what to give to friends and family, what I myself would keep, and what to donate to the School Sisters of Notre Dame at Our Lady of Good Counsel in Mankato. (A fun tidbit: Sister Janet Wermerskirchen kindly instructed me to find "other homes" for anything glitzy with sequins.)

Emotions were unpredictable during the process. Coming across certain items stirred up memories. Sometimes it filled me with calm. Other times, sobs would emerge from the depths of my soul, reminding me how much I missed her. In some cases, it was revealing and intriguing to see what items Mom had kept.

As items made their way to new homes, I reminded myself to be flexible and nonjudgmental about whether people used the gifts or sold them or gave them away in turn. Letting go of the outcome kept me more serene.

Sometimes I found myself needing direction from Mom, so I would ask her spirit to guide me. In some cases, I would ask where to find something or what to do with something. Other times, I would ask for energy, focus, calmness, happiness. Or I would ask for permission to let something move on to another home.

In each instance, I would ask for a physical sign from heaven, and then I would watch for the sign and accept what was delivered.

Not everyone has the skill set to sort through belongings and make decisions. Within your own circle of loved ones, up-front communication about roles and objectives may lead to many peaceful days without arguments.

Within our family, Julia and I worked well together. We found it easy to determine what we each wanted to keep, especially when it came to holiday decor and dishes.

Each person needs to play their unique role. In our example, Dad had no desire to personally go through Mom's clothing or household items. He often read the paper or watched sports while we sorted. What he was wonderful at was delivering items to the people or places designated as new homes. Some of the interactions during the deliveries helped ease his grief and brighten his days. The balance worked well for all of us and kept life moving.

It's funny how space fills. The house didn't feel bare once we moved out Mom's things. Dad enjoyed the new space by spreading out his clothes in the closets.

By going through Mom's things, we opened not only physical space in the house but also emotional space for our grief. We created new energy by moving and sharing Mom's things rather than letting them sit and get stale. The forward momentum helped our grief and assured us that Mom's wishes were being honored.

"Hope" is the thing with feathers -
that perches in the soul -
and sings the tune without the words -
and never stops - at all -

—EMILY DICKINSON

Hospice Bereavement Care
A Lifeline for the Aftereffects

When Mom first enrolled in hospice, we learned that one of the benefits was thirteen months of bereavement care for the family after her death. I emphasized this to Mom. I wanted her to know we would be taken care of after she passed. It took a lot for her to let go of life; knowing we would have support helped ease the process.

The grief counselor indeed turned out to be a blessing. She talked with Dad and me at the house within weeks of Mom's death. By listening to us and acknowledging the process of grief, she opened space for us to have new and challenging conversations.

In particular, she helped us address the upcoming holidays, which we would soon experience without our beloved family member. Together, we explored our feelings about the holidays and considered the motives behind our plans. We also gained clarity about how we could—and should—take care of ourselves and our grief through the activities.

After the initial in-home consultation, we had a few phone sessions with the grief counselor. She also sent us many materials about grief and invited us to grief support events.

We found the bereavement materials insightful. They included other people's stories, tips on how to handle the holidays, a discussion about the signs of grief, reminders to take time for the grief, and ideas about how to be gentle with ourselves. The materials reminded us how grief is widespread—not something only we were experiencing.

Dad especially appreciated attending a few grief support dinners. He valued the social aspect as well as the opportunity to discuss grief and hear others' stories.

I'm grateful for the grief counselor and the opportunity she provided. With her guidance, I was able to take the time to honor the bereavement process in a healthy way.

We delight in the beauty of the butterfly, but rarely admit the changes it has gone through to achieve that beauty.

—MAYA ANGELOU

Gratitude and Goodbyes
Lunch with Dawn from Mayo

Once Mom enrolled in hospice, we no longer had appointments with Dawn, the physician assistant at Mayo. It felt odd, as she had been with us for each stage leading up to that point.

After Mom died, I contacted Dawn to share the news. A few weeks later, I contacted her again and asked if she'd have lunch with Dad and me. My request was twofold. One, we wanted to thank Dawn in person for everything she had done for Mom. And two, we wanted to bring closure to the lung cancer discussion with our trusted advisor.

At the lunch, it was fun to see Dawn's latest hairstyle, talk about the fall season, and hear about her annual Halloween party.

Dad and I gave her a beautiful handcrafted pottery vase with a professionally arranged bouquet of flowers. The gift was a day brightener. We hoped it would remind her of our gratitude each time she saw it.

A sentimental part of the gift was the card. When Mom first shifted to hospice care, Janae and I began working on a custom card Mom could personally send to Dawn. Thankfully, Mom was able to write a special message in the card. But because the hospice time went so quickly, we weren't able to send the card before she died.

At the lunch, Dad and I were honored to present the card on Mom's behalf. It included a photograph of Dawn and Mom together, plus Janae's "You're IT" poem and her quote, "Some people touch our lives briefly, and we change for the better. Others touch our lives deeply, and we're never the same." Inside was Mom's short message, stated humbly and heartfully.

> Dear Dawn,
> Thanks for guiding us on this journey. We trusted you and you helped make the miracle a reality. May God shower you with goodness.
> Love, Patty

From the very beginning of Mom's journey, we had prayed for a miracle—and a miracle was granted. It wasn't a cure, however. Rather, the miracle was how long Mom defied the odds and lived much longer than anticipated. And Dawn was one of the people who helped us recognize that miracle and savor that time.

Dad and I were grateful Dawn gave us the chance to have lunch together. It allowed us to show our appreciation and bring a little more closure to a huge medical chapter. I'm grateful for the quality-of-life-centered approach Dawn brought to the hardest three-year journey of our lives.

How many times do medical professionals hear appreciation from families? Thinking about it makes me want to reach out more often with my gratitude.

*The fact that we cannot see our friends
or communicate with them after the
transformation, which we call death, is no
proof that they cease to exist.*

—WALTER DUDLEY CAVERT

Dragonfly Project Care Packages
Comforting Others in Our Mutual Grieving

About two months after Mom's death, I felt the urge to reach out to our inner circle of family and friends. It was important to stay in touch, even as life without Mom became a new normal. And so I sent them care packages inspired by dragonflies and the Dragonfly Project.

When a friend died of a brain tumor, Anne Marquardt Brooker sent that friend's family Walter Dudley Cavert's story about how dragonflies symbolize the transformation of death. The act touched the grieving family so deeply that Anne founded the Dragonfly Project as a nonprofit organization. She was only eleven years old at the time.

Since 2002, the Dragonfly Project has sent thousands of packets to grieving people all over the world. Each packet contains a condolence card with beautiful dragonfly artwork, a sympathy message, a dragonfly keychain, and the dragonfly story.

The story reminds us that our deceased loved ones are still communicating with us, but they have taken on another form. (To read the story and find out more about the organization, visit https://www.dragonflyproject.org/.)

The dragonfly story has been a lifeline for me in processing my grief. Many years before Mom's passing, Anne spoke at Janae's women's retreat. I was forever changed and have been a supporter of the Dragonfly Project ever since.

Mom knew about the Dragonfly Project as well. She and I wanted to incorporate dragonflies into her funeral plan. Although time moved too quickly for us to bring that idea to fruition together, Janae and I were able to see it through with the help of our friend Sara Weingartner, who is one of the artists for the Dragonfly Project. We featured her beautiful dragonfly artwork on the funeral bookmarks and the thank-you notes.

That wasn't all, though. As fate would have it, dragonflies also worked their way into Father Wilmot's homily at Mom's funeral. I remember Janae touching my shoulder and whispering, "The dragonfly story!" as he began telling the tale. My jaw dropped. We were amazed that the dragonfly story made it into Mom's celebration—as recounted by a true Irish storyteller.

Later, Father told Janae he hadn't planned on telling the dragonfly story—it just came to him while he was giving his homily. He said it was God-inspired. We agreed.

With the dragonfly symbolism and the spirit of the Dragonfly Project in mind, I set out to create my care packages for this inner circle of loved ones. I wanted to reach out to them in their grief—in our mutual grief, as we all loved Mom so much.

To begin, I took a photo of a sculpture at Lake Harriet in Minneapolis. It was engraved with "grieve honestly." Those two words embody a concept I have come to love and often encourage others to embrace.

I printed photos of the sculpture and taped them on the fronts of blank cards. I left the cards blank in the mindful spirit of a loved one passing it on to another grieving person in the future.

Along with the cards, each of my care packages included a Dragonfly Project packet, any of Mom's belongings I may have had for that person, and a letter explaining the significance of the dragonfly story.

Sending the care packages helped my grief journey. I hope the dragonfly—or another special symbol—bolstered my loved ones during that time of grief. Signs and symbols are important, as we will explore later in the book as well.

Strange, isn't it? Each man's life touches so many other lives. When he isn't around he leaves an awful hole, doesn't he?

—CLARENCE IN *IT'S A WONDERFUL LIFE*

A Quilt

Piecing Life Together in New Ways

While much of Mom's clothing found its way to the "Donate" bin, a few things were intimately *Mom*. I didn't want to give them away, and I couldn't imagine myself or anyone wearing them.

The pieces that were "just so Mom" weren't the newest or the oldest or the most valuable pieces. Many times, they were everyday things such as her jeans and the nighties she wore while she was living with cancer. A few were pieces she wore to special events, such as Julia's bridal shower, the Relay for Life, or other family gatherings.

When I told my friend Sara George about these special items, she referred me to a woman who makes quilts with clothing pieces. I thought it was a wonderful way to honor Mom. We had two quilts made.

One quilt hangs in our family lake home. It has a northern-Minnesota feel with lots of flannel and jean materials.

I have the other quilt in my home. It's larger and has many pastel colors. Five years after Mom died, I was in a car accident. I needed to rest often to recover from a concussion. I wrapped the quilt around me and felt comforted by heavenly love and care.

I enjoy showing the quilts to family and friends and sharing stories about the things Mom wore. On our grief journey then and now, the quilts give us a tangible, new way to reminisce about her.

*Cherish is the word I use to remind me of
your love.*

—MADONNA AND PATRICK LEONARD

Wearing a Legacy

My Connection with Mom's Jewelry

In retrospect, I realize jewelry was a focus in my particular story with Mom. I cherish the memory of going through her jewelry with her, even though it was challenging at the time. I cherish the honor of gifting her hand-selected pieces to the special women in her life.

And I especially cherish the pieces I kept of hers.

Jewelry is a long-term, tangible symbol of remembrance. While some of Mom's clothing and shoes have worn out over the years, her jewelry has a permanence that speaks to her everlasting legacy.

I love wearing Mom's jewelry. I think of her every time I put a piece on. Even just looking at her jewelry reminds me of her love, regardless of the monetary value.

Many times, I wear certain pieces if I need extra confidence, strength, or calmness. I often wear the blue-stone ring as a source of strength and connection.

Sometimes Mom's pieces strike up interesting conversations and interactions. Whenever I'm complimented on her jewelry, I find it healing to share that it was my mom's.

We each have our own style with jewelry, and some pieces are timeless while others are trendy. I took some of Mom's jewelry to a trusted jeweler and had new jewelry created for me to wear. For example, we took stones from earrings and rings and had new creations made.

The new pieces are more in line with my style, yet they still carry Mom's legacy. I wear them often, whereas I likely would have just kept the original versions in storage.

I am grateful we decided not to bury Mom's jewelry with her, as some cultures do. By saving them and gifting them to others, we've enabled her pieces to continue to grace lives in a variety of ways. It's what Mom wanted for all her belongings. I know that I myself have found great comfort in staying connected with her in this way.

Experience is what you get when you didn't get what you wanted. And experience is often the most valuable thing you have to offer.

—RANDY PAUSCH WITH JEFFREY ZASLOW

Future Advice

Requests for Encouragement

In the process of going through Mom's belongings, I came upon something in her closet: a special box I had given her not long after she began her cancer journey. Discovering this box was a lesson in outcomes.

Prior to Halloween night 2005, I had always imagined Mom living a long life. She seemed like someone who could live a hundred years. So when her terminal diagnosis revealed otherwise, life became very surreal. My whole vision started to shift.

I kept wondering how I would deal with life without her. I adored the encouraging, loving, fan-club relationship she and I shared. I couldn't fathom not being able to turn to her when I needed support and advice about the ups, the downs, and the in-betweens of life.

Time was limited. Mom and everything she meant to me were limited.

So I wrote down all the topics racing through my mind—all the things I wanted to hear from her, learn from her, hold dear from her. Forever.

I gave her the list along with a box of stationery and a pen. I asked her to write me letters in response to each item:

- *How to prepare before a stressful day*
- *How to calm down after a tough experience*
- *What to think if you die*
- *What to do to help Dad*
- *How to have holidays without you*
- *How to structure my life to stay balanced and grounded*
- *What to do or know if I'm ever:*
  - *Pregnant*
  - *Having a miscarriage*
  - *A mother*
  - *Jealous that others still have their mothers*
- *The importance of staying healthy*
- *How best to get along with others*
- *How to stay positive without your everyday presence in my life*
- *Words to read on holidays when I miss you*
- *Keys to staying positive and looking at the bright side*
- *How to maintain and grow faith*

I wasn't sure what she would write in response, but I envisioned these words of advice and love would be special treasures.

Imagine my reaction, then, when I found the box exactly as I had given it to her.

I didn't find any letters. Everything looked the same as the day I had given it to her as a gift.

I had a sinking feeling.

I wonder why she never wrote the letters. Did she simply forget? Did she run out time—even though I had given her the list two years before she died?

Was it too much to write these final words while still holding on to hope and focusing on surviving her cancer journey? Then again, she never denied the seriousness of her illness nor shied away from end-of-life preparations. She did everything from planning her own funeral to videotaping an interview for future generations. She kept a fine balance between living and preparing for how she wanted to leave things.

I genuinely do not know why she never wrote the letters. Nevertheless, I'm still grateful I wrote that list. As I reread it now, it deepens my self-awareness. It helps me understand my concerns.

If time is limited with your loved one, consider listing your concerns as I did, and then consider asking your loved one to reply with words of advice. Then let go of the outcome.

With faith in our hearts and a rosary in our hands, we can find solutions to the little problems that crop up in our lives each day—and we will be able to triumph over even the greatest struggles and challenges we encounter, no matter how painful, difficult, or hopeless those struggles may seem.

—IMMACULÉE ILIBAGIZA WITH STEVE ERWIN

Spiritual Legacy

Gifting Mom's Rosaries

Mom had a lifelong love of the rosary. When she was a child, her family would often say the rosary together in their home and at church.

Mom correlated moments in life with some of the mysteries of the rosary. When someone was trying her patience, she would say, "She is my cross to bear," and she would seek patience, calling to mind the Fourth Sorrowful Mystery: "The Carrying of the Cross: Patience under crosses."

A couple of days after the funeral, Sara George contacted me and told me about a woman in Wisconsin who made rosary beads by crushing dried rose petals and adding a paste. Sara suggested we dry some of the roses from the funeral flowers and send them to this woman to make rosaries.

I ended up ordering some rosaries and some bracelets for myself and other family members. They would take a few months to complete. Little did I know what I had set in motion by ordering them . . .

In the meantime, I kept finding rosaries as I went through Mom's belongings. I found them in various drawers and purses. She had at least one in her car, along with a cassette of someone saying the rosary so she could follow along while driving.

Mom's love of the rosary touched my heart, though I myself didn't have the same connection. When I offered the rosary cassette to Nora, she in turn asked whether I wanted to keep it. I told her I would never listen to it. I didn't feel like saying the rosary or learning much about it.

I remember reciting it as a family on long car trips to the lake. In reality, it was more like Mom and Dad would be the ones reciting it. As a child, I was always happy to hear the final prayer, because then I knew we were finally done.

When the handmade rosaries arrived from the woman in Wisconsin, I found them to be quite comforting as well as spiritual. They were unique symbols of the past and present. I enjoyed giving them as gifts to loved ones as we grieved for Mom.

At that point, I still didn't realize my love for the rosary was like a small rosebud just waiting to bloom.

Soon after, Janae called to tell me to add a November event to my calendar. The event would be held at the University of St. Thomas, our alma mater.

I distinctly remember Janae's tone. Instead of her usual manner of asking if I'd be interested in going, she came right out and said we were *definitely* going. She felt strongly about us attending.

I followed Janae's lead. Sometimes it could be hard to make decisions amid the confusion of grief, so I often found it helpful when a friend stepped in with some decisive guidance.

I will forever be grateful for Janae being so firm about us attending, because that was the night we met Immaculée Ilibagiza. Named after the Virgin Mary, Immaculée spoke from the heart without any notes for over an hour. Immaculée's love of and belief in the rosary were thrilling and inspiring. Janae and I both purchased CDs of Immaculée saying the rosary—when just weeks earlier I had told Nora I would never listen to a rosary tape.

That was the night my love for the rosary began to bloom. I began a practice of saying the rosary. Every time my fingers slid over the rose-petal beads, I felt a close connection to Mom. I realized that Mom had been guiding me to the power of the rosary all along.

A few years later, Janae and I were blessed to attend Immaculée's weekend retreat. It just so happened to be held at St. Mary's Church in Worthington, Minnesota, where Mom went to church and school for a few years during her childhood. Mom always spoke fondly about Worthington and was grateful to have met her dear friend Gretchen Haberman during that time. Attending Immaculée's retreat in Mom's beloved town felt like another embrace from heaven.

I still find the rosary to be a calming force in my life. It's a form of meditation for me, one I love having as a regular part of my day. I'm grateful for my growing love of the rosary. As it enriches my life on earth, it also gives me a heavenly connection with Mom and Mother Mary.

The best way to spread Christmas cheer is singing loud for all to hear.

—BUDDY IN *ELF*

The Holidays

Grieving the Loss of Mom and Her Traditions

Mom instilled in us a love for the holidays. That first holiday season, we tried to keep everything the same. I, especially, wanted to embrace all our usual traditions in her honor.

We came to realize, though, how tough it is to do everything she used to do. More importantly, we realized how tough it is to carry on old traditions in the midst of grief.

One moment stands out: when we couldn't find Mom's Christmas dishes.

For many years, my aunt Nancy Keenan had given Mom pieces of a certain Christmas dinnerware set. It was fun to see the collection grow, and using the dishes was a wonderful reminder of the special connection between Mom and Nancy. They had each hosted many meals in their homes throughout their lifetimes. So that first year, we of course wanted to use Mom's Christmas dishes—but we suddenly realized that we didn't know where she stored them.

Instantly, grief showered over me and took me by surprise.

I didn't know where the dishes were.

I didn't want to be the one responsible for finding them.

I just wanted things to feel easy, as they did when Mom hosted Christmas.

I just wanted to be mothered.

I just wanted her to still be alive.

Justin and Julia helped me find the dishes. The whole experience was proof of how grief can unexpectedly strike. In my case, I knew it usually worked best to allow myself to just feel the emotion, let the tears fall, and keep going at my own pace.

As we go year to year, we keep figuring out new holiday traditions. We all have our strengths. We're building new traditions, and we've learned to let others go.

Now, Michael and Julia have the Christmas dishes at their home. They lovingly display and use the dishes in December. It's heartwarming.

We know Mom is smiling down on us from heaven as we enjoy holiday meals on her beloved dishes. Often, someone will comment about the dishes, and it's such a positive way to bring memories of her and past Christmas celebrations into our holiday festivities.

Your deceased loved ones are loving, guiding, and protecting you from the Other Side.

—THERESA CAPUTO WITH KRISTINA GRISH

Feathers, Green Lights, and More
Being Open to Heavenly Signs

Physically and spiritually, the circle of life is all-encompassing. When our loved ones pass on to the other side, they often send us signs, symbols, and messages from above. They use these special signs to assure us that they are still part of our lives even though they are on the other side.

We can notice these signs when our senses are heightened—and, quite simply, when we are willing to notice them.

Mom told me a story about receiving a sign after Grandma died. Mom said she was busy getting ready for a trip and helping Grandpa with thank-you notes at the same time. She was running from one thing to the next. As she was dropping the thank-you cards in a postbox at a grocery store parking lot, she started thinking about how tired she felt.

Then, seemingly out of nowhere, a pure-white feather floated down from the sky, right to Mom. No birds were in sight.

Mom instantly sensed that the feather was a message from Grandma saying, "Thank you for all you are doing to help."

From that moment on, Mom had a strong belief that any time she saw a white feather, it was a sign that Grandma was near and serving as a guardian angel.

It was such a gift to hear this story from Mom. I adopted the same mentality and delight in seeing white feathers. Usually, they appeared at just the right time to remind me to lighten up, be nice, or know that I was loved.

Throughout Mom's cancer journey, then, she and I talked about whether she would be able to connect with me after she died. We both hoped she could, and I encouraged her to do so—if possible. We talked about the dragonfly story and its symbolism as well.

After her death, I began looking for signs. I was open to whatever I might receive. I just wasn't sure if there would be one sign, like a white feather, or multiple signs.

I kept looking and looking until one day I noticed that I was getting many green lights in a row while out driving. When I started thinking about it, I suddenly realized that the same thing had happened several times before. For some reason, I was getting an unusual amount of green lights. A glorious amount.

Green lights were signs!

"Thanks for that one, Mom," I said out loud as I cruised under yet another green light.

Now, you might be thinking, *But we all hit a lot of green lights every now and then. It's unusual, yes, but it's still just the law of averages.*

True.

The difference is, I see the magic and meaning behind what other people call averages, coincidences, and synchronicities.

As I was finishing the editing process of this book, I came upon a reference to green lights in David Kessler's *Finding*

Meaning: The Sixth Stage of Grief. It struck me as such a perfect companion to my own green light experience.

> *What did the green light mean? We often talk about "meaning making." Life offers us layers of meaning. We make of them what we will. What meaning did I give to this green light? What meaning did it have on its own? A green light often means it's okay to go.*

My signs from Mom weren't limited to long strings of green lights. I definitely felt them in nature. At times, a dragonfly or a hummingbird would come quite close to me and linger.

Eagles are a spiritual connection for me as well. I often see them and have for years. Mom's sisters, Teresa and Nora, have even commented about how eagles feel like signs to them.

Janae and I had a vivid eagle experience at the lake. Two eagles were soaring right above us, no more than twenty feet over our heads. We could hear the flapping of their wings. We were in awe as they danced in perfect harmony. Chills filled our bodies. It was a holy encounter.

The lake home itself is a place of obvious connection with Mom. I feel her presence there, and I know others do too. It's not a "haunted" feeling. Rather, it feels like an assurance that I am not alone, that I am loved and cared for more than I can comprehend. I wrote many words of this book at the lake.

I especially feel Mom's connection through the sense of touch. When I'm just starting to wake up every morning, I touch my face in a gentle way to welcome her energy and connect with her spirit.

In these moments, I've felt great reassurance that Mom is happy and content. I've also asked her questions about how to handle things in my life. In response, I sense her loving encouragement—and often a bit of heavenly amusement.

One of my favorite things to watch on television are shows about mediums. A medium channels the messages of loved ones on the other side. I find the messages fascinating. I love how the deceased often mention current happenings, assuring us that they are still part of our lives. Though our loved ones are on the other side, we are still connected in other fashions. We need to lean on that assurance.

Another reason I love watching medium shows is that they remind me that others are grieving, just like I am. Mourning can feel isolating and lonely. But medium shows help me feel part of a community—one filled with people who've suffered great loss on that gut-wrenching level I feel.

In addition to watching the TV shows, I have visited a number of mediums since Mom died, and I've experienced a variety of channeling styles and levels of connection. It has been a blessing to find a medium who can create a connection that feels authentic, loving, and helpful.

Seeking signs and feeling immense love in return has been beneficial for my grief. The signs evoke a range of reactions in me: smiling, crying, reflecting, nodding, or even skipping in joy. If I could put words to the signs, they would be: *You are not alone. You are on the right track. You are being guided.*

Signs remind me to thrive, to be jovial.

And to give myself permission to let go of the deep heaviness of losses.

Part 8

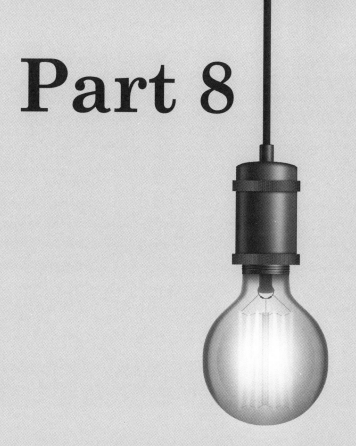

remembrance

This [website] is an excellent idea. You are in our prayers and our thoughts daily. We all love you. Thanks for being a great sister and a loving person.

—UNCLE DAVE KEENAN ON MOM'S
CARINGBRIDGE SITE

CaringBridge Book

Commemorating Our Communication Cornerstone

As weeks transitioned into months, the grief journey transitioned as well. Out of the initial shock and immediate busyness, a deeper and more meaningful experience emerged—one focused on remembrance, commemoration, service, and shared experience.

Months after Mom died, Dad and I deactivated Mom's Caring-Bridge site. But first, we had the entire content of the website printed in a hardcover book through a service CaringBridge provided.

The book documents Mom's journey and also our family's journey with her. It's a good resource for checking details or dates. I found myself turning to it a few times as I wrote this book. The CaringBridge book is also a testament to our wonderful supporters through their guestbook entries.

In retrospect, I'm grateful for Mom's willingness and self-lessness to have a CaringBridge site and to be open about her journey with a mindset of educating others. Her openness eased my grief because it paved the way to receive loving care and support from others.

There are many wonderful posts in the book. One in particular stands out to me. It's from Justin's mother, Sheila Rowland. She wrote it on October 2, 2006:

> *Patty, you look so beautiful in the new photo on the website. Your smile is inspiring . . . I read a quote today in the newspaper that says it all.*
>
> *"I am determined to be cheerful and happy in whatever situation I may find myself. For I have learned that the greater part of our misery or unhappiness is determined not by our circumstance but by our disposition." —Martha Washington*
>
> *You HAVE been and CONTINUE to be INCREDIBLE! As always . . . we are sending love and prayers from Texas.*

Justin's mother died in 2019. Having the above entry between our two mothers has been heartwarming as we grieve for them both. Justin and I strive to apply the Martha Washington quote about disposition to our lives. It's easier said than done at times.

The loss of a mother is like none other.

Expanding your sense of self is the cure for all fear, including the fear of death. When all fear is dissolved, love awakens deep inside us. This is a love that radiates like light from a bonfire, focused on none and denied to none. In this state of consciousness, self-repair and self-healing mechanisms wake up, and our life is transformed.

—DEEPAK CHOPRA

Sharing My Grief Story

The Dragonfly Project Speech

Knowing how much the Dragonfly Project meant to me, Sara Weing-artner approached me about speaking at the organization's 2009 annual celebration. Each year, the event is a remarkable avenue to share thoughts, find solace in music, reflect, and use the symbolism of the dragonfly to help find meaning in our world as well as remind ourselves of the ongoing connection between heaven and earth.

I was honored and touched to be asked to speak. Sharing my grief has been healing for me, just as hearing others' stories has been enlightening and comforting.

In my speech, I touched on the amazing symbols and signs I had received—everything from Mom's white feathers to the green lights to Father Wilmot telling the dragonfly story as if he were reading it straight off the inserts from the Dragonfly Project packets.

I also discussed sending the Dragonfly Project packets in my care packages to Mom's innermost circle and how people quickly and intimately related to the symbolism.

"The dragonfly concept sparks the beginnings of new hellos," I said, "because you are recognizing a presence alive in our lives today. The hellos feel so comforting, reassuring, and encouraging, as they remind us we are not in this alone."

At the end of the speech, I gave a big thanks to the Dragonfly Project for providing an outlet to share our grief journeys together. I called for all to support the Dragonfly Project that day so millions of other grief stories could be told in the future.

I'm grateful for the opportunity to give the speech. I'm also grateful that I accepted the opportunity. Writing and delivering the speech was an important step in my quest to grieve well.

But, at the end, if we are brave enough to love, if we are strong enough to forgive, if we are generous enough to rejoice in another's happiness, and if we are wise enough to know that there is enough love to go around for us all, then we can achieve a fulfillment that no other living creature will ever know.

—HAROLD KUSHNER

Hospice Video

Testifying to the Positive Hospice Experience

In March 2009, Mankato Hospice approached me and asked if our family would be willing to be in a hospice video. We said yes.

Amy Roemhildt interviewed Dad and me in Dad's home regarding our hospice experience with Mom. The video also included photos of Mom, Dad, Michael, Julia, Justin, and me. We were one of three families featured in the video.

During the interview, I shared two questions families can ask themselves as their loved one begins a hospice experience: *How do I want to remember this time?* and *How can I be a gift to the patient throughout this time?*

As I explained, many of us are in uncharted territory during a hospice journey. Keeping the big picture in mind and being a gift in your own unique way are a couple of ways to navigate and stay true to your authentic self.

I also described how the loving memory of our hospice time is coupled with the painfulness of the loss. I'm confident we gave Mom a peaceful departure from this world, thanks to faith, love, teamwork, and commitment.

Being part of the video gave us the chance to help ease other families into the concept of hospice. Our own introduction to hospice was jarring. If a video like this had been available to us, maybe we would have felt more comfortable with hospice. Maybe we would have encouraged Mom to enroll in hospice earlier.

Plus, being in the video opened up conversations with other people about hospice and grief. Sharing our stories and listening to others has been enriching and thought provoking.

Like the Dragonfly Project speech, the video was an opportunity, and I'm thankful I said yes to it. Every time I said yes to an act of service, the experience helped me process my grief and explore more of the emotions around Mom's death.

Electric Days: These are the days each year that have emotional significance for me and can, if I am not aware of them, take me by surprise and result in physical or emotional distress, anxiety or depression. These are the dates that reverberate with memories from my past.

—JANET O. HAGBERG

Mom's First Birthday in Heaven
Reaching Out on an Electric Day

I agree with Janet's description of electric days. I try to be as proactive as possible on days that have special significance to me. Otherwise, the day can take me by surprise and leave me with reactive feelings, behaviors, and communications.

Dad and I anticipated that April 18, Mom's first birthday after her death, would be an electric day. We knew it would stir emotions within us as well as within many others who were grieving.

We decided to acknowledge the birthday, Mom, and our grief by sending something special to our inner circle of friends and family. We had special cards made that featured one of the most unexpected and meaningful gifts I have ever received. The letter inside the card explained it all:

April 18, 2009 would have been Patty Johnson's 66th birthday. While we tenderly miss her, we have a strong sense she's thriving in heaven and finds it delightful.

During the funeral preparation time, my cousin Laura Rheaume and I went to Hilltop Florist to talk about the design of the casket spray. We were lucky to work directly with Noël Van Tol who co-owned the shop and knew Mom. We selected regal colors and were able to showcase many of Mom's favorite flowers. While we were there, Laura and I admired Noël's watercolor paintings.

Two weeks later, Hilltop called me about a delivery. To my heartfelt and emotional surprise, Laura had commissioned Noël to capture Mom's favorite flowers in a beautiful watercolor painting.

It didn't seem right to only have one print, so Dad generously had the enclosed cards made for Mom's inner circle of loved ones. Prints are on display in St. Joseph the Worker Church's Bride's Room and our family's homes.

Enjoy and celebrate life,
Julie Wylie and Doug Johnson

In response, we received many heartfelt thank-you cards beaming with kind words about Mom and sentiments about missing her. Noël's beautiful watercolor touched hearts.

The birthday tribute was a feel-good gesture, as it gave me a chance to spread the joy I felt about the "Patty's Favorite Flowers" painting. More importantly, reaching out on Mom's birthday made that electric day more celebratory than sad.

Be intentional about your electric days. Before one arrives, think about how you want the day to be. Do you want to be alone or be with others? Be quiet or active? Consider what would be ideal.

Be with those who help your being.

—RUMI

Celebration Dinner
Thanking My Angel Network

The evening of Mom's birthday, I invited my friends Nancy, Janae, and Holly to McCormick & Schmick's restaurant in Edina. It was not only a lovely way to celebrate the electric day but also a great opportunity to thank these women for the "angel network" they had set up to support me through Mom's journey. Their prayers, love, gifts, and attention helped me through one of the most intense times of my life. I wanted to gather for dinner as a way to show my appreciation.

When I made the reservation, I was able to include a custom message thanking my friends for all their loving support. The restaurant typed this message as a headline on the menus for our table, which added more fun to the dinner conversation. We had a cozy booth, delicious food, and ongoing conversation.

As a special gesture of my appreciation, I gave matching necklaces to my friends and let them know I had the same one too. The necklaces weren't expensive, but they have been a comforting symbol of our friendship. Over the years, it's been fun to see each of us wear the necklace on different occasions.

I also gave everyone the book *The Necklace: Thirteen Women and the Experiment That Transformed Their Lives* by Cheryl Jarvis and the Women of Jewelia. The book is a collection of moving stories of how a group of women shared a diamond necklace.

It felt great to recognize my angel network's support—and great to just be with them on such an important day. I'm grateful for the gift of friendship. I know the bonds we share have many healing ripple effects that extend to those around us.

In fact, one of those ripple effects occurred shortly after the dinner. Early the next morning, at 4:00 a.m., Janae received an inspiration about how I needed to write a book about my experiences with Mom. That inspiration outlined the book you are reading right now.

You must never underestimate how many people love and cherish you and your family, as it is obvious by this website and the cards you have received. You have accomplished this by the love you have shown all your friends and family. Your strength throughout this is inspiring. We love you.

—MY COUSIN AMY SONDERMAN ON
MOM'S CARINGBRIDGE SITE

Sharing the Journey

Offering Insight and Experience

That same April, Paula Lithander, a coworker and good friend of mine, called me from her doctor's office. She had just been diagnosed with terminal cancer. She said she called me because she knew I was a woman of prayer.

Soon after that conversation, I spoke with Paula again and encouraged her to have a professional photograph taken of herself as well as with her family. Based on my experience with Mom, I explained to Paula that her appearance would change once she started chemotherapy treatment.

In response, she did have photos taken alone and with her family. They were a beautiful addition to her CaringBridge website.

After speaking to Janae about Paula's situation, I decided to create one of Janae's *You're IT! You Make a Difference* tribute books for Paula. I passed the word around the company, and twenty-five people contributed stories, memories, and thoughts to the book.

I sent it to Paula in July. Upon receiving it, she called and said it was the best gift she had ever received.

Paula died that August. The *You're IT!* book was showcased at the memorial, as were her photos. The photos and the memories reminded us of the woman we loved—a happy, strong, and very much alive Paula.

As difficult as it was to lose another cherished person in my life, I was humbly grateful and honored that Paula invited me to share in her journey. Due to my experience of grief and my mom's cancer, Paula felt she could turn to me, she welcomed my suggestions, and she took action she might not otherwise have thought to take.

It reminded me that death is the universal experience that touches us all and that we need to turn to each other in our grief.

I'd seen so many movies where characters sit by beds as their loved ones die. They give speeches, hold hands, and say, "It's okay— you can let go." What none of those books and movies convey is how tedious it is.

—WILL SCHWALBE

Relay For Life

Recognizing Caregivers on the Cancer Journey

Relay For Life is the American Cancer Society's signature activity. Held throughout the United States, these fundraisers place a special emphasis on celebrating cancer survivors as well as remembering those who have passed.

In July 2008, shortly after we heard the *H* word for the first time, I attended the Relay For Life event in Mankato with Mom, Dad, Grandpa Keenan, and his lady friend, Vivian Pfaffinger. It was difficult to admit the end was drawing near for Mom, and it was hard to know what to say to our friends at the relay.

Fast-forward one year. Mom was gone, and Dad and I were chosen to be the Honorary Caregivers for Mankato's 2009 Relay For Life event. This was yet another experience where we could share our grief story with others.

When Dad and I concluded our speech, Relay For Life had a ceremony where we, along with a cancer survivor being honored, held white doves in our hands and released the doves into the air. Doves symbolize peace, renewal, and the link between the physical and the spiritual realms.

As the doves ascended to the sky, the sun broke through the dark summer clouds and shone on our faces. It was an angel moment and a true sign we are loved more than we even know.

The following is the speech Dad and I gave as Honorary Caregivers at the 2009 Relay For Life opening ceremony.

Doug: Thank you. Julie and I are honored and humbled by the recognition today. Before we touch on my wife Patty's cancer journey, we want to congratulate *all the survivors here today*.

Julie: As the American Cancer Society says, "Survivors are proof cancer *can be defeated*."

Doug: There are three survivors in Mankato who are very dear to our family: Jerry Keenan, Patty's dad, cancer survivor nineteen years; Vivian Pfaffinger, Jerry's friend, cancer survivor twelve years; Joe Keenan, Patty's brother, cancer survivor five years. What's incredible is that they are all cancer-free!

Julie: The American Cancer Society has given us such a gift through Relay For Life. Last year, we were here with Mom, and I remember the feeling of relief that she wasn't the only one in sight with a chemo cap on! How many of us—as a chemo patient or when you are with someone in chemo—have felt the chemo-cap stares in malls or restaurants? People often do double takes over cancer baldness. At Relay For Life, we weren't alone.

The relay exudes a safe-haven feeling of belonging, support, and love. I encourage you to take advantage of the chance to share and hear stories while you are here. We may feel alone as families in those doctors' offices, hospital rooms, or our homes, but here we are a community. Strength and inspiration are just a conversation away. We, as a community, are *stronger and wiser* than cancer. Use Relay for Life as a chance to unite. We are not alone.

Doug: Halloween 2005, we were shocked to learn my active, nonsmoking, sixty-two-year-old "healthy" wife had the advanced stages of lung cancer. It didn't take me long to have radon testing done on the house and to install the radon-mitigation system.

As explained by the US Environmental Protection Agency, "Radon is a cancer-causing natural radioactive gas that you can't see, smell or taste. Its presence in your home can pose a danger to your family's health. Radon is the leading cause of lung cancer among non-smokers. Radon is the second leading cause of lung cancer in America and claims about 20,000 lives annually."

Minnesota and Iowa are hotbeds for radon. I encourage you to get your home tested so you can avoid our story.

Julie: Through Mom's entire cancer journey, I only asked a doctor once how long she would live. It is a hard question to ask and a hard one, even for doctors, to answer. I posed the question a day after the diagnosis, wanting to know how to reposition my other life priorities around her life-changing news. The doctor said one year. One year.

Doug: The good news is, she lived longer than one year. She lived almost three years, thanks to prayer, support, chemo, radiation, our positive attitudes, and excellent local medical care.

Julie: Another key factor for Mom outliving her diagnosed time was *hope*. As we see on the T-shirts today, hope is key, and it's through each other's stories we find hope. I remember the day Mom started to have hope. It was in 2005, the day after Christmas—which was always one of our favorite days to shop due to all the sales. We were at River Hills Mall. I had just asked Mom if she wanted to go to Hallmark to buy Christmas cards on sale for next year. She said no. She didn't think she would be here the next Christmas. After all, at Halloween, the doctor said she had "one year."

We were in Herberger's and ran into someone Mom knew. The woman had lung cancer, too, and had lived longer than expected and looked good. I told her Mom wasn't buying Christmas cards for next year. The woman encouraged us to have hope, raved about treatment options, and suggested we buy the Christmas cards.

Because someone shared their story, we became hopeful, bought the cards, and celebrated two more Christmases together.

Time and time again, we were so grateful to those who'd walked the cancer journey prior to us. Who'd paved the way for the American Cancer Society to uphold treatment improvements as well as help develop supportive and informed medical professionals to the thousands of other benefits they provide. Mom's mom, Delilah Keenan, died from cancer in 2001. Mom and I noticed so many improvements in those short years between their cancers—from the drugs that help with nausea to the wigs.

It's the things you don't think about until you need them, but we were so grateful to past cancer patients who figured out how to invent chemo caps that are comfortable, fashionable, and stay put—as well as wigs that look quite natural and feel OK on the itchy, bald scalp.

Doug: We are here as the Honorary Caregivers. And by just looking out over this terrific crowd, we can tell many of you are caregivers. We see it in your nods during our story, the way you are helping someone walk on the grass or find a seat. We see it in your eyes. We know our stories overlap with common themes, concerns, joys, fears, and pains.

Julie: I want to share a caregiving story that is etched in my heart. We were all at the lake home three weeks before Mom died. I had done a range of things to help Mom during that trip. I did some things—specifically, helping in the bathroom—that I had never imagined or considered doing for another person. But when a person is in need, we rise to the occasion. *And RISE, we caregivers do!*

Well, Mom was seated comfortably in the living room. I went over to her and asked her if she wanted anything. She said, "I just want *you* to be happy."

I just want you to be happy.

And it hit me: my happiness—me taking care of myself as well—was something else she needed from me as a caregiver. And at that moment, I wanted to go outside and read in the sun. So, I did.

It was such a strong wake-up call that caregiving truly demands a team approach. If you've found yourself in a caregiving position, continue to reach out for help. You might be surprised who steps up to the plate. If you aren't caregiving, think about how you could add to the happiness of a caregiver or how you could become a caregiver.

Now, even after Mom's death, the word *hope* is taking on another meaning for us. For us, *HOPE* also stands for Honoring Our Patty Evermore. We are passionate about honoring Patty's legacy by sharing her story to teach and encourage others before, during, and after important life transitions. We are grateful to Relay For Life for allowing us to share our hope with and for you.

Doug: Thank you for supporting Relay for Life. It's not lost on us how incredible things do happen through God's loving hand. Thank you.

You and your family are in Gerry's and my prayers every day. I am lucky to have such a wonderful big sister like you.

—AUNT TERESA SEVERSON ON
MOM'S CARINGBRIDGE SITE

Seeing the Fruits
The Endowment in Action

Mom's dream of an endowment fund spanned nearly her entire cancer journey. The seeds were planted with Mary Ann Brandt. We nourished the dream as our connection with Youth Frontiers came together in the final weeks of Mom's life. And then the memorials came in after Mom's death, making the fund grow in incredible ways.

In fall of 2009—a year after Mom's death—we began to see the first fruits. There was enough money available for a staff Honor Retreat for the faculty and staff of the Mankato Loyola Catholic School. Then in 2010, we began rolling out a series of grade-specific character-building retreats. The various retreats focus on honor, kindness, courage, respect, responsibility, and wisdom.

The beauty of the endowment is threefold:

It creates a targeted focus, per my parents' requests, for the memorial gifts and inspires us to donate regularly to keep the momentum going.

It allows our family to confidently carry out Mom's wishes, which are so clearly stated in the legal endowment agreement.

It lets Mom's memory live on through the retreats and the other benefits of the funding.

The endowment has been a wonderful way to honor the memory of Mom's life. I'm amazed at the effects it's had in the years since her death, and I marvel at the potential positive effects in the future.

The endowment fund even had a direct effect on me—one I never expected. I attended the 2009 Honor Retreat, and it was an amazing experience. Many people thanked me wholeheartedly for the day and commented about missing Mom or how their teaching was inspired by her example. It was incredibly healing and comforting for my grief journey to be around people who knew Mom and talked about her.

I doubt Mom realized that would be a side effect from setting up the endowment. But now it is a cherished part of my life.

Our loved ones live on in us.

—AUNT NORA KEENAN

Final Thoughts
Cherishable

Thank you for being on this journey with me. You, the reader, have been in my heart ever since I wrote the first word of this book. I hope this book has been a light in the darkness, helping you see that life is cherishable.

Time is cherishable.

You are cherishable.

I can appreciate you might be feeling that hope is beyond your reach. I felt the same way with my grief journey at times. The pain was unbearable. At times, it's still heartbreaking.

I've heard that when someone is grieving, they need to tell their story multiple times. For me, that involved everything from unexpectedly telling a Target cashier, "My mom recently died," to giving that prepared, rehearsed speech onstage at Relay For Life in front of hundreds of people.

This book, of course, has been a way to share my story and to cherish Mom's life. A true teacher, she taught us great life lessons in the way she lived her life, which included her cancer journey and her passing. My family and I can only hope our lives will be as impactful to others as her life was to us.

Again, I hope this book has been a guiding light inspiring you to cherish the time you've been given with your loved ones. Most importantly, I hope it's been a light inspiring you to share your own grief story in whatever way you feel comfortable. By opening to others, you embody love and maybe lighten their burdens. You open yourself and possibly others to healing and transformation.

May sharing our stories bolster our spirits and enrich the concept that we are all connected.

*You and I have to trust that our short
little lives can bear fruit far beyond the
boundaries of our chronologies. But we have
to choose this and trust deeply that we have
a spirit to send that will bring joy, peace, and
life to those who will remember us. Francis
of Assisi died in 1226, but he is still very much
alive! His death was a true gift, and today,
nearly eight centuries later, he continues
to fill his brothers and sisters, within and
without the Franciscan orders, with great
energy and life. He died, but never died. His
spirit keeps descending upon us. More than
ever I am convinced that death can, indeed,
be chosen as our final gift of life.*

—HENRI J. M. NOUWEN

Acknowledgments

When you score, you better start pointing.

—ABBY WAMBACH

Deep appreciation for my dad, Douglas Johnson, for his encouragement throughout my life. I have vivid childhood memories of being onstage at the end of school band concerts and seeing my dad be the first to rise and start a standing ovation, regardless of how we sounded. It brings tears to my eyes. That kind of love instilled confidence to believe in myself.

Heartfelt gratitude to Justin Wylie, Nora Keenan, Michael Johnson, Julia Johnson, Janae Bower, Holly Locher, and Kelsi Zellinger for their loving help along the way with this book as well as the willingness to read the early manuscript and provide thoughts and suggestions. Thanks to Nancy Gnos for reading the final manuscript prior to printing. Also, I'm grateful for my deep friendships with authors Janae Bower and Alain Hunkins, who provided steady currents of coaching and understanding for every phase of writing and publishing.

The book in itself is an acknowledgment and tribute to the many cherished souls who were part of our journey with Mom.

It was an honor to specifically name people within the book, and many others bolstered our spirits as well. Feeling the power of community is a golden experience.

Loving thankfulness to the friends and family members who supported my calling to write the book. Support took many forms. You are part of this creation if you ever did any of these things with or for me: cleaned, cooked, baked, hugged, listened, cried, laughed, encouraged, celebrated, shared your heart in a card or gift, welcomed me into your home, visited me in my home, walked and talked, went out to eat, covered for me at the office on my vacation days, checked in on me, discussed books, kept in touch, shared in support groups, or sat with me in church.

Abundant kudos to the team at Pond Reads Press (in alphabetical order):

Angela Wiechmann, editor, for the divine gift of immersion editing and for foreseeing how the book would flow best for the readers. Pulling the floss story out of me was one of the many miracles that occurred along the journey, thanks to Angel.

Athena Currier, book designer, for her flexibility. I originally thought the cover would be teal and pink, but then I experienced Michele Wylie's hospice journey and death in 2020, and I realized that the colors of chocolate and cream better fit how I was feeling.

Becca Hart, publishing coordinator, for the warm communications.

Betsy Barthelemy, who conducted the final critical read, for catching the various ways I tried to spell *mindset*.

Hanna Kjeldbjerg, project manager, for helping with the title and subtitle to ensure Google searches would connect readers in need of my book and for dazzling me with her own use of language and descriptions.

Lily Coyle, publisher and owner, for explaining the process of working with her company and for believing we could work together on my book.

Ruthie Nelson, proofreader, for her keen eye and for saving me from dangling modifiers, among other things.

And finally, loving compassion to my readers. I cherish you. May you have epiphanies of ways you are able to cherish and be cherished. Because we are all cherishable.

Final Words from the Author

Upon reflection, I am reminded of how life continues to ebb and flow.

People die.

Babies are born.

Cats meow.

The details of my life change.

The undercurrent of my life and what guides me through the details is my mission statement. Through participating in retreats, seminars, and mentorships led by Janae Bower, Sue Krautkramer Whelan, John Gessner, and Janice "Hope" Gorman, I've created my mission statement. It's been a rock to stand on in my dark and light times.

And it goes like this:

Enjoy the Joyride from God.

I am enjoying and thriving in life as an unconditionally loving, wise, and abundantly thinking light being.

I am living, loving, and communicating authentically with a lavish purpose of embracing God's calling in doing things much greater than myself as well as letting the gifts in each of us shine.